Instructor's Manual for

Statistics

FOURTH EDITION

Instructor's Manual for

Statistics

FOURTH EDITION

David Freedman
Robert Pisani
Roger Purves

W. W. Norton & Company
New York and London

Copyright © 2007, 1998, 1991, 1978 by W. W. Norton & Company, Inc.

Cartoons by Dana Fradon.

Printed in the United States of America.

ISBN 0-393-93012-2
ISBN 13 978-0-393-93012-2

W.W. Norton & Company, Inc., 500 Fifth Avenue, New York, N.Y. 10110
http://www.wwnorton.com
W.W. Norton & Company Ltd., Castle House, 75/76 Wells Street, London W1T 3QT

1 2 3 4 5 6 7 8 9 0

Table of Contents

Introduction

	What's New in the Fourth Edition?	1
	Why Did We Write this Book?	1
	Scheduling	4
	Exercises	5
	Supervision	6
	Grading	6

How to Use the Book

Part I	Design of Experiments	7
Part II	Descriptive Statistics	8
Part III	Correlation and Regression	14
Part IV	Probability	18
Part V	Chance Variability	20
Part VI	Sampling	26
Part VII	Chance Models	35
Part VIII	Tests of Significance	37

Answers to Review Exercises

Part I	Design of Experiments	44
Part II	Descriptive Statistics	46
Part III	Correlation and Regression	53
Part IV	Probability	59
Part V	Chance Variability	66
Part VI	Sampling	72
Part VII	Chance Models	83
Part VIII	Tests of Significance	85

Test Results

From the First Edition	103
From the Second Edition	118
From the Third Edition	132

This manual is not for resale.

Please do not photocopy solutions.

See page 6.

Introduction

What's new in the fourth edition?

For the fourth edition, new expository material was added at crucial places. For instance, the first section of chapter 26 was completely rewritten. Some other famous difficulties have been handled a little better too, and there are new problems on topics of current interest. But the principal change is to the data. Statistics, like people, show wear and tear from aging. Fortunately or unfortunately, data are easier to rejuvenate.

Why did we write this book?

The world is full of elementary statistics books. Why did we write another one? The answer is that we came to want a book which would explain the basic ideas in the subject to an intelligent but nonmathematical reader, and make the ideas vivid through real examples. These objectives seem innocent enough; achieving them turned out to be much harder than we had expected. We proceeded largely by trial and error, going through many cycles of classroom testing and revision before first publication in 1978. Each successive draft was used for a year with many hundreds of Berkeley undergraduates, in courses at different levels of difficulty (with or without a calculus prerequisite), the class sizes ranging from 30 to 300.[1]

Each year, we watched the students working on the materials, listened carefully as the friendlier ones told us what was wrong with the exposition, and scribbled frantically away at the next year's draft.

Along the way, we were forced to notice some unpleasant facts. The first shock was discovering how much trouble the students had with arithmetic. In self-defense, we started giving pre-tests. By now, such tests have been given to several thousand

---

[1] The book was mainly developed in the Statistics 2 course at Berkeley. This course, which is divided into two or three large lecture sections, enrolls about 500–1000 students each semester, drawn mainly from the social sciences and the less-quantitative natural sciences. Still, about 40% of these students have taken a calculus course, and 20% of them have completed two or more additional college-level mathematics courses. The book is also used in Statistics 20, 21, and 131. Statistics 20 has class sizes of 30–150; virtually all students have had calculus, and about half are in quantitative fields like mathematics, statistics, computer science, and engineering. Statistics 21 is a large lecture course for business students, with about 300 students. Statistics 131 is an upper-division course for students in the social and life sciences, with class sizes in the range 30–60.

students. Here are four questions from the pre-test.[1]

1. 300 is what percent of 2,000?

2. $\sqrt{100,000}$ is about:
    (i) 30   (ii) 300   (iii) 1,000   (iv) 3,000   (v) can't tell

3. In the United States, 1 person out of every 500 is in the navy and one-sixth of naval personnel are officers. What fraction of the United States population consists of naval officers? Or can this be determined from the information given?

4. A quart of vodka is 40% alcohol. Write a formula for the percentage of alcohol in a mixture of V quarts of vodka and J quarts of orange juice.

Only three students in four can do the percentage in question 1, and only two in three can handle the square root in question 2. Question 3 tests whether they know when to multiply fractions; only one student in four gets it right. Many elementary statistics texts claim their sole prerequisite to be "high school algebra." Question 4 is a very gentle probe into what the students remember from high school algebra: one student in six can write down the formula.

The pre-test even seems to understate the problem. One issue it misses is reliability. A student may be quite good at doing one-line arithmetic problems, like

$$\sqrt{2500} = \underline{\qquad}$$

But an exercise that requires doing half a dozen steps of similar difficulty is rather a different project. Another issue is context. When students have trouble deciding which arithmetic operations to perform in response to word problems, many stop being able to do arithmetic at all. It is as if they get exhausted during the analysis phase.

Now when we started writing, we tried to teach the conventional notation,

$$\frac{1}{n-1}\sum_{i=1}^{n}(x_i - \bar{x})^2$$

and all the rest. But it soon became clear that the algebra was getting in the way. For students with limited technical ability, mastering the notation demands so much effort that nothing is left over for the ideas. To make the point by analogy, it is as if most the undergraduates on the campus were required to take a course in Chinese history—and the history department insisted on teaching in Chinese.

So we decided to try writing in ordinary English. For three probabilists, this presented some unexpected difficulties. And it led to a surprise in the classroom: the students wanted the equations, even though they found the symbolism baffling. Perhaps we shouldn't have been surprised. Nonmathematical students seem to flounder in numbers courses. They survive only by ruthless pragmatism. Their objective is to pass the final. Usually, the final is a series of word problems, and the course is seen

---

[1]   Pretests from 1977, 1988, and 1995 are reproduced at the end of the manual. Over the period, there have been many changes in admissions standards, but the pre-test results have stayed about the same.

as a series of equations. The instructor may think that the equations express some general truths, but this tends to be lost on the students. For them, the main issue is learning how to associate the equations in the course with the word problems on the final, and recognizing which numbers in the word problem are to be substituted for which variables in the equation. There is a Berkeley student word for this syndrome: *pluginski*.[1]

By the time students get to a statistics course, pluginski is so ingrained that anything like an equation tends to shortcut thought: students just grab the equation and run. Without equations, students really have to work at understanding the concepts in order to solve the problems. This is exactly what we want to achieve, even though the students find it irritating. As a result, whenever possible, we banish equations.[2] However, in many cases we do have a substitute: short summary sentences for the major points. There is a definite advantage to this approach: it is hard to memorize an English sentence without paying some attention to what the words mean.

By now, we had been through several drafts, and thought the worst was over. It wasn't. By our lights, we had succeeded in translating quite a lot of statistics into acceptable English. But, as we discovered, the students were still having a hard time with our materials. We got discouraged enough to start grumbling to colleagues in other departments, showing them the "easy" passages the students couldn't read. The colleagues couldn't read them either. Where we saw simplicity, they saw a maze of complexity.

This was a low point, but things improved from there. We realized that the problem wasn't "dumb students"; it was more a case of nonstatisticians seeing the world very differently from statisticians, needing different kinds of explanations, and wanting to learn different kinds of skills. Very few members of our audience are actually going to derive formulas, or carry out large scale data analysis. Many, however, are going to have to deal with statistical findings, because nowadays it is hard to read research journals—or even newspapers—without coming across statistical arguments.

We began to rethink our strategy. We had been making a tacit assumption, that the exposition should start from the points which were clear and obvious— "elementary"—to us, building up to more complicated and interesting ideas. However, elementary mathematical points are often rather hard, even when expressed in English. Insisting on these points just confuses things and distracts attention from the main issues. Also, we were still focusing on the procedures, leaving it to the students to infer the purposes of the activities—the scientific questions being answered. This is fine for people who find technique easy, and therefore have time to think about what they're doing. For our readers, students and nonstatistical colleagues alike, this was a failure.

We decided to start at the other end. What are the main ideas that our field has to offer the intelligent outsider? Everything else, no matter what its technical interest, had to be set aside. Then, the reader has to be persuaded that each idea is

---

[1] The phrase of the new millenium is *plug'n chug*.
[2] Some instructors who have used the book do the equations in lecture, and tell us the students accept this as complementing the text.

worth knowing. To do that, we had to make explicit the question behind the statistical procedure. Often, we were able to find some vivid example embodying the question. Similarly, many statistical concepts formalize some understanding about the world; and in many cases we were able to find the right example to crystallize this insight. Once motivated, the ideas had to be presented in reasonably smooth language, free of annoying technicalities. And it all had to be fitted together into a coherent narrative, so that at each stage the reader would know enough to appreciate the next question.

Carrying out this program turned out to be a real adventure, because it forced us to reconsider the basics of the field from a different perspective. In the end, we think we brought it off. The book covers a good set of topics for a first course, arranged in logical order, and properly illustrated by examples. It works quite well for us, and for many friends who have tried it elsewhere.[1] Sample tests, with pass rates, are reproduced below.[2] As far as we can see, the book is intelligible to its intended audience: nonstatisticians who want to learn some statistics in order to go about their affairs. This includes students in college classrooms—as well as professionals in other fields.

To some statisticians, the book looks like an easy read—too easy to use as a college text. This criticism is off the mark. The material is not easy. We know from our courses that students, even those with good mathematical preparation, have to work quite hard to read the book and solve the exercises. In part, this is because there are many pedagogical difficulties we just could not overcome. Then too, statistics does involve some deep ideas. Instructors who use the book will have to help their students master those ideas.

Scheduling

At Berkeley in the 1970s, Statistics 2 was taught in ten-week quarters, with three hours of lectures a week, and three hours of laboratory. In the 1980s, the university went back to fifteen-week semesters. The book can be used successfully with both calendars. It is written so that most chapters take about an hour of lecture time. However, this is a fairly quick pace. To maintain it, the more difficult sections in some chapters have to be skipped, or carried over to a second lecture.

There are 29 chapters to the book, so something has to go to fit it into a quarter. In a semester, the whole book can be covered; there may even be some time to spare

---

[1] Indiana, Minnesota, Sonoma State College, Stanford, UC Los Angeles, UC Santa Barbara, Utah State, Winnipeg, Wisconsin, Yale.

[2] In typical Statistics 2 finals, the class averages were around 60 out of 100, with an SD of 20. Students with calculus averaged around 65, each additional college mathematics course contributing around 2 points to the average. On similar tests, Statistics 20 students, who know calculus and are majoring in quantitative fields, averaged about 70. Most of the test questions were taken from exercises in the book, so the students had seen them before. An interesting sidelight: about 70% of the Statistics 2 students take the course to fulfill a requirement; the others take it voluntarily. Those taking it as a requirement only averaged about 55; the volunteers averaged over 65.

at the end, to do some of the mathematical formalism. Dependencies among the various parts of the book have been minimized in the writing, leaving instructors fairly free to pick and choose. As far as we are concerned, the logical core of the book consists of—

Chapters 1–2	Design of experiments
Chapters 3–4–5	Descriptive statistics
Chapter 13	What are the chances?
Chapters 16–17–18	Chance variability
Chapters 19–20–21, 23	Sampling

We see chapters 1, 2, and 19 as the most important. The big point is that the design of a study determines its reliability, and likewise for samples.

Sometimes when we teach the course, we cover parts I–VII, but omit part VIII on testing. At other times, we have covered everything except part III (correlation and regression). A third strategy, which we can recommend, is to cover the whole book, omitting—

Chapter 12	The regression line
Chapter 15	The binomial coefficients
Chapter 25	Chance models in genetics
Section 26.6	The t-test
Sections 27.3–4	The z-test for experiments
Chapter 28	The chi-square test

Exercises

We discovered early on that unless we could write an exercise to test a point, students were not likely to learn it. So we worked quite hard to create a variety of good exercises. Most sections close with an exercise set, the answers being at the back of the book. All chapters but 1 and 7 include a set of "review exercises." In many chapters, the review exercises cover previous material too. This prevents the material from disappearing, and makes the students learn to judge when the different procedures apply. Answers to the review exercises do not appear in the book, but are in this manual, below. We usually make out homework assignments from the review exercises, and put some of them on the tests as well. Generally, we assign about half the review exercises in the book as homework.

Most exercise sets include a few problems which can be solved by a straightforward application of the procedures just covered in the book. However, there usually are harder problems too. Some exercises, for instance, ask the students to choose among competing procedures, or decide whether a proposed procedure is sensible. Other exercises ask the students to make rough guesses as to the magnitudes of certain quantities, still others call for qualitative judgments. Such exercises cannot be solved by mechanical application of formulas: they require understanding. In the student vernacular, these are "concept questions."

Many exercise sets can be used as diagnostic aids, to pinpoint the difficulties students are having with the concepts. We often get the students to do the exercises in laboratory periods, working together in small groups. We go around from group to group, talking to them about what they are doing. The exercises provide a good framework within which to discuss the ideas we want to get across.

Supervision

One key to teaching a large lecture course is supervision of the teaching assistants who handle section meetings (or "labs," in the Berkeley vernacular). Our experience is that TAs want to lecture. Not unnaturally, they want to teach mathematics, and are a little impatient with our nonmathematical approach. On the other hand, we think we've already given the lectures, and just want the TAs to help the students work problems.

To make this stick, we drop in on the labs from time to time, and observe the TAs at work, or talk to the students ourselves. More formally, we meet the TAs once a week, and review with them the problems to work in lab. This means going over the statistical content of the problems, and the pedagogical issues: what does this problem illustrate? where is it discussed in the text? what will students find hard? how can you break the problem down into smaller pieces? These sessions and the lab visits were eye-openers—for us and the teaching assistants alike.

Grading

At Berkeley, the students turn in homework; this is graded by "readers," often undergraduate majors.[1] The readers work on a very tight time-table, and come out of a tradition where word problems have numerical answers which are right or wrong. However, we want solutions to be written out in reasonable style, with the logic explained.

Some of the answers at the back of the book are quite complete, and could serve as models for students handing in assignments or tackling exam questions. Others are sketchy. Generally, we provide complete answers for some of the questions in each section, particularly those covering new material. Similar comments apply to answers in this manual.

The focus is on the concepts. When grading, we do not penalize students for minor numerical errors. For many of our students, interpolating in a table is a lot of trouble. So we tolerate rather crude rounding. This attitude may have affected some of our numerical solutions.

We tend to write out complete solutions for assigned homework, or delegate this task to the TAs. These solutions—not the Instructor's Manual—go to the readers. Solutions are returned with the graded homework. The readers are then better able to judge what we want from the students, and there is less chance of solution files appearing in the student community. For similar reasons, we ask you not to circulate material from this manual.

---

[1] When budgets have to be cut, university management tends to view readers in lower-division courses as a luxury; managers think differently from the rest of us.

How to use the book

This section of the manual has detailed comments on the different chapters in the book, outlining the contents, pointing to nonstandard language and pedagogical difficulties.

Part I. Design of Experiments

The material in part I of the book is interesting and not very technical, so we find it a natural introduction to the subject. The material looks easy, and students may get the wrong impression. Some instructors may wish to start right in with descriptive statistics (part II), and talk about design issues as they come up. The book is organized with that possibility in mind.

Chapter 1. Controlled Experiments

This chapter explains the key elements in a randomized controlled double-blind design, and why each is necessary. The context is the Salk vaccine field trial. Other examples are presented to reinforce the ideas. Conventional wisdom dictates that the investigator should control the key variables and randomize the rest. The text focuses on the randomization, which is the hard idea. Some instructors will want to pay more attention to the possibility of controlling variables by stratifying subjects before randomization.

Chapter 2. Observational Studies

In this chapter, observational studies are distinguished from controlled experiments. With an observational study, it is harder to draw conclusions about cause-and-effect relationships. The "cause" and "effect" may both be the result of some hidden third factor—a confounder. We return to confounders in chapter 9. Students often seem to interpret a "confounder" as any alternative explanation for an effect. Of course, the idea is more subtle: in order for X to confound the association between Y and Z, X has to be associated both with Y and with Z: that is the point of section 5. See exercise 8 on p. 22 or exercise 10 on pp. 26–27. (Note 9 to the chapter has more discussion.)

Notes on review exercises. Exercises 1 and 2 may seem unnecessary, but many students do not realize that you take percentages to adjust for differences in group sizes. Some such students think that with a bigger denominator, the percentage will be bigger; others, perhaps more sophisticated, think the reverse. The usual recipe for computing percent—$\frac{a}{b} \times 100\%$— obscures the idea that a percent is a rate: 10 percent means 10 per 100. (Exercises 14–15 on p. 24 teach this idea.) We regret to say, however, that the idea will probably get overwhelmed by the repetition of $\frac{a}{b} \times 100\%$.

Many of the review exercises are tough, because students don't see any alternative explanation to the causal one; or, they find a "confounder" that is not associated with the putative cause. We keep editing the problems to make our points more sharply. Even so, many students will have trouble; they are not used to reading at all carefully. In grading, we aren't sympathetic to rote repetition of slogans—even ones we believe, like "association isn't the same as causation." Exercise 12 covers Simpson's paradox (section 2.4).

Notes on lecturing. Instructors have asked us how we handle this part of the book in lecture, and we have done it several ways. One is to give a straightforward presentation of the material: each chapter can be covered in one lecture, omitting a section or two if time runs out. There are enough ideas here for the students to benefit from lectures as well as reading. Another approach is to bring out the main ideas in discussion. Take the Salk vaccine field trial, for example. We present the background to the trial, as outlined in the text. Then we say:

> Suppose they gave the vaccine to everybody, and the incidence of polio went down. Would that show the vaccine was effective?

The class usually figures out why not. Then we present the design which puts the consent group in treatment and the no-consent group in control and ask about that. The first objection is almost always that the treatment and control groups are different sizes. After dealing with that, the class will figure out that the two groups will differ in some more important way, although they may not be able to say exactly how; we explain that polio is a disease of hygiene (p. 4 of the text). Then we present the NFIP design (grade 2 in treatment, grades 1 and 3 in control), and ask for comments on that. We talk about running a proper controlled experiment, and ask the class whether the assignment should be done by the toss of a coin, or by expert judgment. Then we go on to talk about placebos and double-blinding; these ideas are hard to elicit.

If the class is too small or too large, discussion can collapse; however, we have had good discussions with classes ranging from 20 to 200 students. The length of the discussions has never been a problem: if time runs out we just drop some sections in the chapter, assigning them for reading. On the other hand, an instructor who wants to present additional material on design will find many examples in the exercises; others are cited in the footnotes.

Part II. Descriptive Statistics

For students, descriptive statistics is much easier to understand than probability or inference, and it may be a more important topic. This part of the book is about descriptive statistics for one variable—the histogram, average, standard deviation—and their relation to the normal curve.

A first pass is made at the topic of measurement error, in chapter 6. This may seem out of place in an introductory course, but it embodies one of the great lessons of statistics: every empirical number is subject to error, whether it is generated in a physics lab, a market survey, or a census. If the number is determined again, it comes out a bit different. In fact, the variability in repeated measurements is a basis for judging the likely size of the error.

Chapter 3. The Histogram

The main object of this chapter is teaching students how to read a histogram, but we found this hard to do without also teaching them how to draw one. Drawing a histogram—or any graph—is hard work. Students will need pencil, graph paper, and eraser (or a computer with a graphics package and an eraser tool). At first, students will have to be helped with the rudimentary mechanics, like laying out axes. We talk about "class intervals"; some instructors find "bins" and "bin widths" less intimidating.

We originally tried to fudge the definition of a histogram, but kept getting caught in contradictions. Eventually, we were forced to follow the definition quite strictly, which is perhaps unusual in an elementary text. For us, percentages are represented by areas. In this setup, the height of a histogram shows crowding or *density*. The word "density" has a technical sound, and is downplayed for that reason. Moreover, the units—for instance, % per $1000—are complicated; we couldn't get around that. Our experience is that "% per $1000" goes down better than "%/$1000."

There are two advantages to the area approach:

- There is only one kind of histogram to deal with (other books move from "frequency" to "relative frequency" to "density").
- The histogram can be matched up against the normal curve so that area under the curve becomes intelligible.

Histograms will be used a lot in this book, so it is important to get the students used to looking at them.

Chapter 3 also introduces the idea of a *variable*, with the following classification:

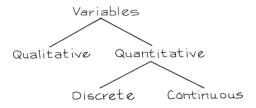

Our students didn't seem to like this much, but then they didn't seem to like any distinctions. (Perhaps they lack the experience needed to appreciate the usefulness of the distinctions, and don't want to be examined on things they don't quite grasp.)

Notes on review exercises. Exercises 1 and 4 teach the interpretation of histograms. Exercises 2 and 3 are for practice in drawing the graphs. Exercise 5 is about the density scale, and 6 shows how the histogram groups the data—and blurs distinctions within groups. Exercises 7–12 are hard. Exercise 7 makes them look at the tails of a histogram. Number 8 is about the difference between histograms and bar graphs. With number 9, students explained the spike at 2 by the fact that lots of respondents gave 2 as the GPA. This is now the answer to parts (a–b). Part (c) therefore has to have another answer. With number 10, students will prefer explanations in terms of any real factors—epidemics, immigration, whatever—to the statistical explanation in terms of digit preference. Likewise, the statistical explanation for number 12 (few very hot days) will not be obvious.

Notes on data. Some instructors use data sets of their own to illustrate the statistical techniques discussed in the book; this works out well. Some do stem-and-leaf plots on small data sets before presenting histograms, and report good results from this approach.

Notes on graphics. Liberal use is made of smooth curves to indicate the shapes of histograms (as on p. 34), and some students will need reassurance about this. The point of sketching the histogram is usually to show some qualitative feature, such as the weight in the tails. For this, a smooth curve is just as good as the histogram, and is easier on the eye (sketch below). In general, the art work has been kept fairly informal, in the hope that working diagrams will not look too forbidding.

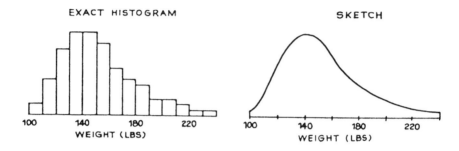

Chapter 4. The Average and the Standard Deviation

The chapter focuses on interpreting these two statistics. "Standard deviation" is abbreviated to "SD," read "ess dee." *Variance* is not introduced, for two reasons:

- Students get confused between Var and SD— "Is SD = $\sqrt{\text{Var}}$ or Var = $\sqrt{\text{SD}}$?"
- Var comes out in the wrong units, and the wrong order of magnitude.

For instance, American men average 190 pounds in weight, with an SD of 40 pounds. So the variance of weight is—1600 square pounds. To a mathematician, taking the square root is an easy fix. However, we think it is quite hard to visualize the impact of a square root (or even a linear transformation), without actually doing the arithmetic. For instance, is 17 degrees Celsius warm or cold? In a Fahrenheit world, you might reach for a calculator before answering.

So we decided to focus on the SD, deferring the concept of variance to later courses. And even before presenting the calculation of the SD, the book explains the interpretation: the SD measures how far away, on the whole, the numbers are from their average. This interpretation can be fleshed out in the usual way:

- For many lists of numbers, about 68% of the entries are within one SD of average, and 95% are within two SDs.

The book points out that this rule isn't exact or universal. We hope it won't be misconstrued as slavish devotion to the normal curve. In fact, it works surprisingly well for many data sets that don't follow the normal curve at all (footnote 10 to the chapter). We often talk about the SD as the "typical" departure from average, and hope instructors will not mind the potential confusion with "probable error"—a concept not used in the book.

The root-mean-square operation is presented in section 4, as a mathematical preliminary to computing the SD. In fact, taking the r.m.s. is a basic operation in statistics. For instance, it comes up again for the regression line (chapter 11). We used to introduce it there, but found that the students had a terrible time distinguishing between the r.m.s. error of the regression line and the SD of y. Moving the r.m.s. forward helped solve that problem—but caused a new one: some students now confuse the r.m.s. and the SD. This is easier to sort out (exercises 9 and 10 on p. 73) but the instructor should be prepared to help.

Students may ask, "Instead of doing the r.m.s., why not just drop the signs and average?" We do not have such a good answer, except to say that the r.m.s. fits in better with the theory; orthogonality is discussed in note 8 to the chapter, but that is a tough sell. Later in the course, instructors can explain that with large samples, it is the SD of the population which determines the asymptotic distribution of the sample average around the population average. Competing measures of spread, like the average absolute deviation from average, just won't do the job (footnote 9 to chapter 18).

The technical definition of the SD, as the r.m.s. deviation from average, is presented on pp. 71–72. This reinforces the interpretation of the SD as a measure of the overall size of the deviations from average. Test results indicate that virtually all the students learn to calculate the SD correctly. But if not made to practice, they forget the algorithm within a few weeks. The book only teaches the "r.m.s. deviation" procedure for computing the SD. Another one,

$$\sqrt{\overline{x^2} - \overline{x}^2},$$

is mentioned on p. 74. We used to explain this, as well as procedures for grouped data, but only managed to confuse the students and make them learn less rather than more. They never seemed to believe that the two formulas would give the same answer, so they worried about which one to use, or combined them in unfortunate ways:

$$s = \sqrt{\frac{1}{n}\sum_{i=1}^{n}(x_i - \overline{x})^2 - \overline{x}^2}.$$

For us, alternative formulas represent a diversion from the main objective: teaching the students how to use the SD. After all, computers make it less important for people to learn efficient algorithms—you just have to enter the data and push a button. The trick is interpreting the output.

Notes on review exercises. Many of the exercises focus on the qualitative ideas. Exercise 3, for instance, requires students to make a rough guess as to the answer: this forces them to think, instead of rushing to the formula and plugging in. Exercise 12 is hard, because students won't fit it into the cross-sectional vs. longitudinal framework.

Notation. When working at the blackboard, we write "ave" and "SD." We no longer use $\bar{x}$, s, μ or σ in the beginning courses—too exhausting for the audience.

Which SD? The text defines the SD with n (the number of entries in the list) in the denominator, rather than $n-1$. The $n-1$ is introduced much later (section 26.6) as one of the modifications needed to handle small samples. We felt that in the main line of exposition, there should be only one formula for the SD. To see why we went for n, consider the average of m draws made at random with replacement from the box $-1, +1$. When m is reasonably large, this average will be in the range $-1/\sqrt{m}$ to $+1/\sqrt{m}$ with probability about 68%. We want this interval to be of the form $\pm\sigma/\sqrt{m}$, where σ is the SD of $\{-1, +1\}$. So, the SD of $\{-1, +1\}$ has to be computed with 2 in the denominator, not $2 - 1$. In other words, when calculating the SD of a population in order to determine the asymptotic behavior of the sample average, the right denominator is n.

The conventional argument for $n - 1$ is that $\frac{1}{n-1}\sum_{i=1}^{n}(x_i - \bar{x})^2$ is unbiased. So it is, unless a regression is involved, in which case $n - p$ is needed. And the minute someone takes square roots to get the SD, bias comes back. We know it looks old-fashioned, but n is the right denominator for present purposes.

Chapter 5. The Normal Approximation for Data

This key chapter ties together histograms, the average, the SD, and the normal curve. The passage on pp. 80–81, which justifies the 68%–95% rule, is difficult to teach. For instance, take figure 2. The shaded area under the histogram between 60.5 inches and 66.5 inches represents the percentage of women with heights in that range, which is the interval within 1 SD of the average. By inspection, the shaded area is about equal to the area under the normal curve between -1 and 1. This last area is 68%, justifying the rule. However, when asked, "What does the area under the histogram between 60.5 inches and 66.5 inches represent?", many students will respond "68%." Their anxiety to get to the numerical answer shortcuts the logic. Review exercise 1 of chapter 3 is designed to prevent this; also see review exercise 5 in the present chapter. (Review exercise 1 in chapter 4 is designed to help with the language: "the percentage of entries within 1 SD of average" isn't exactly student English.)

Our method for teaching the normal approximation is graphical. On the blackboard, we draw diagrams just like the ones in examples 8–9 on pp. 85–87. Unless pushed, students seem to resist drawing these diagrams (or any others). Then later on in the course, with more complicated problems, they lose track of which areas they want. The diagrams help.

Section 4 takes up percentiles. It also shows that many histograms are far from the normal curve, a point which comes up again in section 6.3. The point is important, because some students take the word "normal" very literally indeed (p. 89 of the book). For this reason, we try to avoid phrases like "normal histograms," saying instead "histograms which follow the normal curve."

Section 5, on finding percentiles for the normal curve, will be tough going for some students. This material is used again—glancingly—in part III. However, exercises on percentiles are interspersed with later material.

Note on terminology. In this book, a histogram "follows" the normal curve if it is close to the curve.

Notes on review exercises. Exercises 10–11 are hard. To help students work exercise 11, we ask them to mark (by eye) the average on the histogram, as well as the region within one SD of the average. Then we get them to work out ave $\pm$ SD, using the values given in the problem.

Chapter 6. Measurement Error

Students may confuse chance error and bias. They may also need help in seeing that the SD of a series of repeated measurements gives the likely size of the chance error in each one (pp. 100–101 of the book, and chapter 24).[1]

The text has the equation

individual measurement = exact value + bias + chance error.

Some tact is needed when presenting this, because many students want to solve for the unknowns on the right, and feel cheated when they discover this to be impossible. The equation is a useful conceptual tool. Even though the unknowns cannot be precisely determined, they can often be estimated quite well.

Outliers are discussed in section 3, emphasizing the point that many histograms just do not follow the normal curve.

Notes on review exercises. The special review exercises cover most of the ideas in parts I and II. Exercise 3 may make standard units more vivid; #4 is not easy, due to the interplay between numbers and percents. Exercises 6–7 prove difficult for students who want to operate formally with the SD, instead of seeing it concretely as a measure of spread. Such students think the SD should stay the same. To help, we tell them to think about having all the men and women in a classroom, then sending the women out; what does this do to the spread in heights? Exercise 9 is a warm-up for #11 on p. 138.

With exercise 10, the HANES data are cross-sectional, so the older people in the study were born earlier, when there was more social pressure to be right-handed. This exercise, like many others in the book, may provoke students who want a self-contained mathematics course, free of background facts. Exercise 12 illustrates digit preference; also see exercise 10 in chapter 3. Exercise 13 was edited, to make it easier and to bring out the points more sharply: the elegant fact about the uniforms is now part of the exercise. Exercise 14 raises some interesting issues about the design of clinical trials. This is a hard one: students often say that the bias favors screening, "because there will be more cancers to detect and more lives saved." In exercise 15, the tables are quoted from the source, and the numbers really do not add up.

Chapter 7. Plotting Points and Lines

The presence of this chapter may be a bit of a shock. However, many of the elementary statistics students at Berkeley have trouble with graphs. Some teachers may want to spend an hour on this chapter. Our approach is to review points and lines as we cover part III; students who need extra help can read chapter 7 by themselves.

---

[1] "Likely size" is just meant to convey similarity in magnitude: chance errors similar in size to the SD are common; chance errors several times larger than the SD are quite rare. The same point comes up again on pp. 16 and 20 below.

Part III. Correlation and Regression

This part of the book is about bivariate data—scatter diagrams, the correlation coefficient, and the regression line. The treatment is purely descriptive. Many teachers may wish to postpone or even skip part III. It is possible to move directly from part II to chapter 13 (probability), and then to part V (chance variability). It is also possible to do just chapters 8 and 10 from this part of the book. However, part III does follow naturally from part II, and it is easier for the students than parts IV–VIII.

In chapter 8, the correlation coefficient is presented as a key descriptive statistic needed to summarize the relationship between two variables. Then r is used to get the regression line going in chapter 10, and to determine the spread around the line in chapter 11. We used to do the regression line before introducing the correlation coefficient, but this proved too mathematical for the audience, and we had a hard time explaining r after presenting the line. For instructors who think of regression equations as invariant across data sets, with the SD of the residuals—and hence r—as situation-specific, our order of topics may seem a bit artificial (note 9 to chapter 12). If so, please bear with us.

Chapter 8. Correlation

The main job is to teach students how to read (and draw) scatter diagrams. Then, *association* is discussed carefully. Students who work exercise set A on pp. 122–24 will get comfortable with these ideas. Next, the correlation coefficient is interpreted graphically, as measuring clustering around a line. It is clearer to say that r measures clustering—rather than spread—because as r goes up to 1, clustering increases while spread decreases. Scatter diagrams are summarized by the five statistics on p. 126; the warning about outliers or nonlinear association is deferred to section 9.3. Section 8.4 gives an algorithm for computing the correlation coefficient. We do not discuss r^2: the fraction of variance explained by a regression is at bottom a rather mysterious statistic. See D. A. Freedman, *Statistical Models* (Cambridge, 2005, §4.3).

Note on terminology. We found it helpful to introduce two nonstandard terms:

- The *point of averages* (ave. of x, ave. of y) picks out the center of the scatter diagram (p. 125).
- The *SD line* indicates the drift of the scatter diagram (section 8.3). This line goes through the point of averages, and its slope is (SD of y)/(SD of x); the sign is the same as that of r. (If r is 0, either sign can be used.)

Many nonstatisticians (and some statisticians) who fit a line to a scatter diagram by eye will approximate the SD line rather than the regression line. The contrast between the two is the regression effect (section 10.4). For us, the main point of the SD line is to help in defining the regression effect.

Notes on review exercises. The graphical interpretation of r is covered by exercises 1, 7 and 8; the computation of r, by exercise 9—although part (c) can be done qualitatively. Exercises 2 and 5 are about association. Exercises 3–4 and 11 try to get at the connection between r and linearity. Exercise 11 is not easy; to help students work it, we ask them to plot some data points. Exercise 9 on p. 106 was preparatory; so were exercises 7–8 on p. 130, but these turn out to present interesting difficulties of their own. For instance, with #8, students want r to measure the impact of hypothetical changes in incomes, rather than the association between incomes in a fixed data set.

Chapter 9. More about Correlation

Section 1 explains that r is a pure number, invariant under scaling, symmetric in x and y. (The last point has some force, because students will interpret r as a measure of causation.) Since r is invariant under change of scale, "clustering" must be interpreted relative to the SDs. This is somewhat delicate, as indicated by figure 3 on p. 145. Section 3 explains that r may not be useful if there is a strong nonlinear association, or outliers.

Section 4 discusses the ecological fallacy—the idea that individual behavior can be inferred from group behavior. (The term "ecological" is mysterious, and is downplayed in the text.) This may be a controversial section, because many investigators in the social sciences use ecological correlations without batting an eye: see notes 3 and 4 to the chapter for some cites.

For many students, a real intellectual effort is needed to compute r. They conclude that it must be a very powerful tool. It is. But there are limits, and section 5 points some of them out.

A subliminal theme in this chapter is *attenuation*, the reduction of r due to restriction of range or measurement error. See exercise 9 on p. 144, exercises 1–2 on pp. 145–46. Ecological correlations generally exceed individual-level correlations: this is attenuation in reverse—at least, if the individual-level data are obtained from group averages by adding noise.

Notes on review exercises. Exercise 4 is on attenuation-in-reverse. Exercise 9 discusses the relationship between student evaluation of TAs and student gains in learning; the correlation is negative. Exercise 10 is a little trick. Students tend to "explain" the negative correlation between SAT scores and percentage of students taking the test by saying, "students did worse in the states where more of them took the test." That is the answer to the first question in part (a), so a different response is needed for the rest. Exercise 11 is about ecological vs. individual correlations; exercise 12 helps students to interpret different regions in a scatter diagram.

Chapter 10. Regression

Section 1 presents a verbal equivalent of the regression equation for estimating the average of y from x. If x goes up by one SD, on the average, y does not go up by a whole SD, but only by part of an SD, namely, $r \times$ SD of y. Section 2 develops a more intuitive feeling for the regression method, using the graph which displays the average of y against x. This is called the *graph of averages*. Exercise 1 on p. 163 shows the graph for incomes of husbands and wives. Section 3 takes up regression estimates for individuals, along with percentiles (which are a bit difficult). The material on percentiles can be skipped, although some of the later review exercises cannot then be assigned. Exercise 4 on p. 168 paves the way for exercise 7 on p. 567, and demonstrates that there can be some art to examining scatter diagrams.

The regression fallacy is discussed in section 4. This is the most interesting—and difficult—idea in parts II and III. When x goes up by one SD, most people want y to go up by a full SD too. The fact that it doesn't is the regression effect. The text explains that the regression effect is due to the spread of the scatter diagram around the SD line: see figure 5 on p. 171 and figure 6 on p. 172. People resist this statistical explanation, and want some real cause for the regression effect: that is the regression fallacy. The regression effect is implicit in section 1, but there it is kept in a very low key; we wanted the students to learn the mechanics before confronting the mystery.

Section 5 explains that there are two regression lines, one for y on x, another for x on y. There is ample room for confusion here. For example, in figure 8, the regression line of height on weight is steeper than the SD line; how come? (Answer: weight is plotted on the vertical axis.)

Notes on review exercises. Exercise 1 helps students interpret regions in the scatter diagram; also see review exercise 12 in chapter 9. Exercise 2 tries to connect regression estimates for groups and for individuals. Many students will do the same arithmetic twice—and feel puzzled; we want them to make the connection (section 10.3). Exercises 4 and 7–8 demand a real understanding of the regression effect, and are difficult. Exercises 9 and 10 are on percentiles, the latter putting another spin on the regression effect.

Note on the regression equation. The equation behind the prose treatment is

$$\frac{y - \bar{y}}{\text{SD } y} = r \frac{x - \bar{x}}{\text{SD } x}.$$

We used to teach the equation. Students would ask what r meant, as well as SD x and SD y, to say nothing of $\bar{x}$ and $\bar{y}$. This was fair enough. Then they would ask what x was, at which point we got a bit discouraged. Finally, they would ask what y was. We gave the equation up as a bad job.

Note on terminology. The "graph of averages" is not a standard term, but we found it useful in discussing the regression line. In principle, this graph depends on how finely you subdivide the x's.

Chapter 11. The R.M.S. Error for Regression

This chapter introduces residuals, as well as the formula for the r.m.s. error of the regression line: the r.m.s. error is interpreted as the amount by which a "typical" point deviates, up or down, from the regression line. (Compare pp. 10–11 above, on the SD.) Students may want to know why they need both r and the r.m.s. error: one answer is that r is in relative terms—relative to the SDs—while the r.m.s. error is in the same units as y. Residual plots are taken up in section 3, although their power only becomes apparent with multiple regression.

The definition of "homoscedastic" on p. 190 is a problem for some students. As far as they can see, the scatter diagram in figure 8 (p. 191) shows more spread in a strip over 68 inches than in the strips over 64 or 72 inches. They are using range to measure spread. The range is bigger in the middle of the diagram, because there are more people there. This is taken up in the text when homoscedasticity is defined; also see exercise 8 on p. 71.

For "football-shaped scatter diagrams" (bivariate normal distributions) section 5 shows how to calculate the distribution of y when x is confined to a narrow strip: of course, that is the conditional distribution of y given x. The calculation is a bit intricate. Students will have a hard time connecting the r.m.s. error and the "new SD:" the first is global, describing the whole diagram; the second is local, describing one strip. Exercises 1–3 on p. 193 are designed to make the connection. Many students will ignore the heteroscedasticity in exercise 3, and just do the arithmetic. The lesson continues with exercises 4–6 (p. 194). Exercise 4 requires the students to interpret the strip in the diagram. Exercise 5 requires estimation of averages, SDs, and r by eye. Exercise 6—which is the punchline in this series—makes you look at the local SD; part (b) is intended to ward off the obvious misinterpetation—that the SD of *any* subgroup is smaller than the SD of the whole. Exercise 7 on p. 195 is a real puzzler—the regression effect in acute form.

The focus of chapter 11 is descriptive, not inferential. The r.m.s. error measures the spread of the points around the regression line. The chapter does not consider uncertainty in the position of the regression line, which increases with distance from the point of averages; see note 5 to the chapter. Despite the relatively narrow focus, chapter 11 will take some time to teach.

Notes on review exercises. Exercise 8 is about measurement error; a common student response to (a) is "to see the regression effect." Charitably interpreted, this isn't so bad; the point is that the two measurements are likely to differ. Exercise 10 requires students to see that regression estimates fall on a line. Exercise 11 requires the students to look at a scatter diagram—and use what they know about U.S. schools. (Compare figure 5 on p. 39.)

Chapter 12. The Regression Line

The regression equation is presented in section 1, as an aid to computing: the exercises were set up with this in mind. The slope and intercept of the regression line are interpreted as descriptive statistics, with a warning about confounding. Section 2 discusses fitting a straight line to data in order to estimate the slope and intercept of an ideal linear relationship, and makes the point that the regression line minimizes the r.m.s. error. This material will not be easy. Section 3 restates the difficulties in drawing causal inferences from slopes. Exercise set B tests the understanding of the material in section 2; also see review exercise 8.

Review exercises 9 and 10 are hard, because students do not recognize the regression line from its description. We encourage them to sketch a scatter diagram for the income-IQ data, find the point of averages, draw the line defined by the exercise, and mark the strip corresponding to children with the given IQ. Then we ask the students to find the center of that strip. Exercise 11 makes the point that the regression line goes through the point of averages. Special review exercises 1–17 at the end of chapter 15 cover the material in chapters 1–12, and will be of interest to instructors who give midterms covering the first 12 chapters.

Part IV. Probability

As probabilists, we like the subject a lot; but students find it confusing. And whatever the advocates of the new math used to say, sets and functions make things worse for beginners. We also found that very little probability is needed to handle the statistics presented later in the book. So we went back to a more primitive approach. Chapter 13 handles the basics—independence being the most important idea—and sometimes we skip the rest of part IV. Section 14.1 on counting and chapter 15 on the binomial distribution help just a little, when setting up probability histograms in chapter 18. Students will realize that there is some depth to the material, when they hit part IV. Manifestations of "test anxiety" are to be expected.

Chapter 13. What Are the Chances?

Section 1 explains the frequency interpretation of chance. We could only afford one interpretation, and this seemed to be the smoothest. We hope that colleagues who belong to other schools of thought will not be offended. Section 2 presents conditional probabilities. Example 2(a) responds to students who have trouble thinking about the chance that the second card dealt from a deck will be the queen of hearts: "What's the first card?" So we try to explain what an unconditional probability is, which takes a bit of work.

Section 3 does the multiplication rule. Independence—the key idea—comes in section 4. *Collins* is discussed in section 5, showing that the assumption of independence matters. This opens one of the major themes of the book. When does the theory of chance apply? What happens if the theory is used in a situation where it does not apply? The application to DNA testing is mentioned on p. 234; the chapter notes give citations to the literature.

Notes on review exercises. These exercises are simple and qualitative, in order to encourage thinking about the issues. (Displays of professional cleverness are especially disastrous when teaching probability; the students just wonder how they'll ever manage.) Exercise 2 is puzzling to some readers: we explain that it is harder to jump two hurdles than one.

Exercise 7, from Kahneman and Tversky, points to a common misconception. Exercise 9 asks for the chance of not getting 10 sixes on 10 rolls of a die. Many students will answer this by calculating the chance of getting 10 non-sixes, $(5/6)^{10}$. (From their perspective, the opposite of 10 sixes seems to be—no sixes.) To help such students sort things out, we ask them if the dice can land so as to get some sixes, but not 10 of them. We try to elicit concrete answers, e.g., 3 sixes followed by 7 aces. Part (c) is a further effort to sort out the confusion. Exercise 11 prepares for expected values and box models.

Notation. On the blackboard, we write fragments like "chance of heads" or "ch. of ace on 1st roll and ace on 2nd roll." We try to avoid "P(A)," "P(heads)," "A ∩ B," "red ∪ black."

Chapter 14. More about Chance

Thinking about the set of all possible ways that a chance experiment can turn out is a very useful technique, and section 1 presents it. Section 2 has the addition rule. Example 5 is non-trivial, because many students want the chance of getting at least one ace in two rolls of a die to be $1/6 + 1/6$. The double-counting argument is a bit abstract; at this point, the sample-space representation of chances would be quite powerful, and figure 1 is a reasonable substitute.

Section 4, on the paradox of the Chevalier de Méré, is an example of how to compute probabilities using the method of complements. Students find this a bit too clever: instead of being impressed that the problem can be done at all, they are annoyed at not having a simpler way to do it.

The focus in chapters 13 and 14 is qualitative, getting across the new concepts of "independent" and "mutually exclusive" events, and trying to separate them. Students have a hard time with these two ideas. After all, both seem to express ideas of unrelatedness; there is a natural temptation to merge any two new ideas: and another temptation to think that if one doesn't apply, the other must. Exercises are designed to ward these temptations off, with partial success; and see the "FAQs" in section 3. Moreover, basic probability really does involve fractions, and this may demoralize some students.[1] The rest of the book features decimals, which are easier.

Notes on review exercises. Exercise 3 may seem like over-kill; trust us, many students still don't get it. Exercise 4 teaches that two chances are better than one; after all, that is why students like midterms. Exercises 5 and 6 help distinguish between "independent" and "mutually exclusive" events. The language—"all," "not all," "none"—is still foreign to the students; that will be the key difficulty in exercise 11. (Exercises 1–2 on p. 250 may help.) Exercise 12 will get to them, because they have trouble separating conditional and unconditional probabilities. Exercises 13 and 14 are quite subtle.

Chapter 15. The Binomial Formula

This chapter explains how to calculate binomial probabilities. We skip the derivation of the coefficients; some instructors may wish to do this in class.

Notes on review exercises. Students want to scan the problem, grab the numbers, and run to a formula. You can't do probability that way, or statistics either. Many of our problems (like number 9) are set up to defeat the student strategy. Exercise 11 brings in the sign test. The context is twin studies on the health effects of smoking. (Also see exercise 6 on pp. 258–59.) The sign test is an attractive introduction to significance-testing, but there is a hitch. Students want to get the P-value by computing the probability of the observed outcome. They do not like tail probabilities, and who can blame them? We prefer to deal with this issue in a setting where the chance of any particular outcome is too small to be interesting (section 26.1).

The special review exercises cover all of parts I–IV. Exercise 3—from the *Bouman* case—is a variation on Simpson's paradox. Exercise 6 reinforces the distinction

---

[1] According to the NAEP, only 68% of the seventeen-year-olds in school in the United States can add 1/2 and 1/3. Berkeley students can add fractions; even for them, however,

$$1/2 \text{ of } 1/3 = 1/2 \times 1/3 = 1/6$$

is rote learning—"of means times." For proof, see the pre-test results.

between cross-sectional and longitudinal studies. (The Current Population Survey, of course, is cross-sectional.) Older people were born earlier, got less education, and their skills may have become obsolescent. Students want to "explain" the results in terms of employment status: older people work less. So, in this edition, we consider only people working full time. Exercises 7 and 9 involve percentiles; one of the difficulties in number 7 is that students will not be quite sure about the difference between "percent" and "percentile." In exercise 10, the data were extracted from the CPS file, with no hitches. The idea is to prevent the students from saying, automatically, that every diagram in an exercise is wrong. In exercise 13, many students will want r for diagram (i) to be nearly 1, because there is a strong—nonlinear—association. (Exercise 3 on p. 148 gave some warning.) Exercise 16 (by Amos Tversky) is a cunning example of the regression fallacy. Exercises 15 and 17 cover material in chapter 11; these are hard.

Part V. Chance Variability

One famous difficulty in teaching elementary statistics is getting across the idea that the sample average is a random variable. Randomness, after all, is quite a complicated idea. It is easily overwhelmed, either by the definiteness of the data, or by the arithmetic needed to calculate the average.

In our experience, the most intelligible short explanation goes something like this:

> You took a sample and computed the average. That is a number. But it could have come out a bit differently. In fact, if you did the whole thing all over again, it would come out differently.

This variability is the key point to get across, and it tends to be obscured by the technical sound of the phrase "random variable." As a result, we have given that phrase up—and many other hallmarks of civilization too. For the phrase, at least, there is a good substitute: drawing at random from a box of tickets, where each ticket has a number written on it. This may seem crude, but conveys a clear image.

To bring variability into sharper focus, we use the idea of *chance error*. For instance, when we talk about the sample average (chapter 23 in part VI), we tell the students:

> Draw some tickets at random from a box, and take the average of the numbers you get. This will be close to the average of all the numbers in the box, but it will be a little bit off. This amount off is *chance error*:
>
> average of draws = average of box + chance error.

How big is the chance error likely to be? This question is answered by a number we call the *standard error* (abbreviated to SE, read "ess eee"). The upshot is that the average of the draws will be around the average of the box, give or take an SE or so. Technically, a "chance error" is the difference between a random variable X and its expected value $E(X)$. The "standard error" of X is $\sqrt{E\{[X - E(X)]^2\}}$. (At the risk of the obvious, the formula disappeared from the text at a very early stage, followed soon after by the random variables themselves.)

"Standard error," of course, is not the usual term; most authors use "standard deviation" both for data and for random variables. In our experience, however, students have a lot of trouble separating the standard error for the sample average from the SD of the sample. Calling the two by the same name makes it hopeless. So in this book we are quite rigid:

- The SD is for data.
- The SE is for random variables.

Some instructors prefer the more conventional terminology; we ask their indulgence in this matter among many others.

Drawing tickets from a box, chance variability, expected values, standard errors, the normal approximation. . . . That is a lot of ideas. It takes times to get them across, and it is very hard to deal with them adequately in the middle of a complicated discussion on sampling. So we develop these ideas first, in part V, focusing on the sum of draws made at random with replacement from a box.[1] We start with the sum because chance variability is easier to recognize for sums than averages.

We handle chance variability with more care than is common in elementary books. Our pedagogical motives should be clear by now: the ideas are hard, and need time to sink in. But we also have to admit an ideological motive. We think that statistical inferences should be based on explicit chance models, for reasons given in the text; sections 21.4–5, 22.5, 23.4, 24.4, and 29.4–5.

Now students are busy people, slightly cynical, with a definite short-term goal: passing the final. Their previous mathematical education stresses arithmetic procedure, not logical deduction. It is useless to tell them, "Statistical inferences should be based on chance models." This is empty rhetoric, with a lot of fancy words: no sensible exam question can be based on that kind of statement. We want students to take chance models seriously, so we spend course time on the topic. We also have exercises where getting the model wrong leads to the wrong answer—and losing points.

A final remark. Part V is independent of part IV. Instructors who want to spend the minimum amount of time on "pure probability" should, in our opinion, skip part IV but do part V. Part V only takes three or four hours of class time, and it is a very good investment.

Chapter 16. The Law of Averages

Students often think that with a good sample, the sample percentage will equal the population percentage. This makes it difficult for them to appreciate the standard error calculations in part VI. Part of the trouble is that they don't understand chance variability. Section 1 of chapter 16 takes this up. We have a coin. On each toss, it is as likely to land heads as tails. Now we toss it 10,000 times. Are we likely to get exactly 5,000 heads? Surely not. As the number of tosses goes up, the difference between the number of heads and the expected number tends to get larger and larger

---

[1] Technically, this is our substitute for a sum of independent, identically distributed random variables. We are sacrificing some generality: our random variables only take finitely many values, with rational probabilities. That is quite enough.

in absolute terms, that is, as a number. However, the difference tends to get smaller and smaller in percentage terms, relative to the number of tosses. For many students, this distinction is new and difficult. It is central to the careful discussion of the law of averages in section 1. This section also discusses the concept of chance error, with the equation

number of heads = half the number of tosses + chance error.

The *likely size* of the chance error is used informally in the text. (The technical equivalent is the standard error.)

The balance of the chapter is spent setting up box models and introducing the sum of the draws from the box. A box model consists of draws made at random from a box of tickets; each ticket in the box shows a number. The chance variability in coins, dice, roulette wheels (and later, sampling processes) is related to the chance variability in draws from a box. Eventually, this produces real economy of thought: there is a general theory, instead of a lot of special cases. At first, students find this approach rather strange, but they quickly get used to it.

Many examples in this chapter are based on gambling at roulette: the sum of the draws from the box corresponds to the net gain. For instance, take example 1 on p. 283. The net gain in 100 plays at roulette, staking $1 on a single number at each play, is like the sum of 100 draws from the box:

$$1 \text{ ticket } \boxed{\$35} \quad 37 \text{ tickets } \boxed{-\$1}$$

The phrase "is like" has a precise technical meaning: the net gain and the sum have the same probability distribution. Of course, we do not insist on this in the text, but make the point through problems like exercise 6 on p. 281 or exercise 2 on pp. 284–85.

Students find the gambling interesting, although a bit technical. (One touchy point is adding up negative numbers.) It is a digression from the mainline statistical issues. However, setting up a proper model for a mainline statistics problem is hard. Setting up a model for roulette is much easier, and it's good practice. As we tell the students, the first step is to write the box down. (Of course, you can quickly generate a lot of free-floating boxes; nobody said this was an easy subject to teach.)

Notes on review exercises. Exercise 1 tests the distinction between absolute and relative errors, and will be easier for the students when translated into a problem about coin-tossing. Exercises 4, 6, and 9 are variations on the law of large numbers; the last may have some technical interest (note 6 to the chapter). Exercises 7 and 8 are about box models, and #10 foreshadows chapter 23.

Chapter 17. The Expected Value and Standard Error

This chapter presents the formulas for the expected value and standard error for the sum of draws made at random with replacement from a box. The first idea is that the sum of the draws from a box will be around its expected value, but will be off by a chance error:

sum = expected value + chance error.

The likely size of the chance error is given by the SE for the sum. As we write over and over again on the blackboard,

The sum of the draws will be around _____ give or take _____ or so.

There is a downside: some students will later view expected values as random variables, computed up to some margin of error. Among other things, after the sample has been drawn, students will want the expected value for the *parameter* to equal *the estimate*. Given our (slavish?) devotion to the frequency theory, we developed many ward-off exercises. See, for instance, exercise number 6 on p. 294, number 8 on p. 328, number 1 on p. 366. . . .

We tell the students that chance errors of an SE or so in size are fairly common, but chance errors bigger than several SEs in size are very unusual. The SE for the sum of draws made at random with replacement from a box is computed by the square root law (p. 291) as

$$\sqrt{\text{number of draws}} \times \text{SD of box}.$$

Students need help seeing what the square root means: when the number of draws goes up by a factor of 100, say, the SE for the sum of the draws only goes up by the factor $\sqrt{100} = 10$. In particular, as the number of draws goes up, the SE for the sum goes up in absolute terms, but goes down relative to the number of draws. When the number of draws is large, the normal approximation can be used (section 3), although a full discussion is postponed to chapter 18. Exercise 8 (p. 297) reinforces the law of averages, and may have some appeal on its own: see note 6 to the chapter.

As a matter of style, it is wise (though cumbersome) to write "SE for sum," not just "SE." (We try to make the students do this, although we often sin by omission.) Later on, we will have both the SE for sums and the SE for averages. Students will want to merge those two entities. Insisting on full names helps prevent this.

Many boxes in gambling problems (roulette, for instance) have only two kinds of tickets, and there is a short cut formula for the SD of the box. More technically, if $P\{X = a\} = p$ and $P\{X = b\} = 1 - p$, the SE is

$$|a - b|\sqrt{p(1 - p)}.$$

This formula appears (in words) on p. 298.

We attempt to treat standard errors in a unified way, tracing everything back to sums. In section 5, a coin lands heads with probability p and is tossed n times: what is the standard error for the number of heads? This problem fits into the general framework of sums by the 0–1 coding trick, counting heads as 1 and tails as 0. The number of heads is like the sum of n draws made at random with replacement from a box where the fraction of tickets marked 1 is p, and the fraction marked 0 is $1 - p$. The SE for the sum is, of course, $\sqrt{n} \times$ the SD of the box: now use the short cut.

Unfortunately, the 0–1 coding isn't so simple, in part because adding up 0's and 1's only seems sensible to mathematicians. So the section goes through the coding in some detail. The students have trouble remembering to put 0's and 1's on the tickets. This isn't so bad with coin-tossing: some numbers are needed, 0 and 1 seem reasonable. It is harder when rolling die and counting the number of 6's, still harder when taking a sample and counting the number of high-income people. In such examples, the students may already be thinking about some quantitative variable: 0's and 1's pale by comparison. The "classifying and counting" slogan should help, and so does the cartoon on p. 301.

There are two other downsides to the 0–1 coding:

(i) When computing the SD of a 0–1 box, students insist on the factor "$1 - 0$" in the formula $(1 - 0)\sqrt{p(1 - p)}$. They love substitution; it's what they've been trained to do in math courses.

(ii) Students may automatically change to 0's and 1's, even for quantitative data. (The crunch comes in part VIII.) To help students use 0–1 boxes only when needed, we try to mix up the exercises a little. For instance, review exercise 9 in chapter 21 is on quantitative variables, even though chapter 21 is about qualitative variables. Conversely, review exercise 5 in chapter 23 involves qualitative data.

Section 5 closes by relating the law of averages to the square root law. It is the square root which makes the SE for the number of heads go up in absolute terms, but down in relative terms. Chapter 17 has a lot of material, and it may spill over into a second lecture. (On the other hand, chapters 16 and 18 go fairly quickly.) We put some emphasis on the idea of "observed values," introduced on p. 292. Also see, for instance, exercise 4 on p. 293, or 4 and 7 on p. 303–4. We think this will help when it comes to statistical inference in parts VI–VIII.

Notes on review exercises. Some students have trouble getting started on exercise 4: the connection between percentages and probabilities may be problematic. Exercise 9 will be difficult for students who think that two games with the same expected value must offer the same chance of winning. This exercise should demonstrate why the SE is needed. (For a preview, see exercise 4 on p. 299.) The contrast between expected and observed values is drawn in exercises 6 and 12. Number 10 focuses on the $\sqrt{}$ in the square root law. Number 11 is a hard exercise on setting up box models, as is #14. Number 13 is an interesting variation on the law of large numbers (perhaps too interesting).

Chapter 18. The Normal Approximation for Probability Histograms

We introduce probability calculations for sums through the normal curve. When the number of draws is large, there is about a 68% chance for the sum to be within one SE of the expected value, and so on. This topic is broached in chapter 17 and discussed in chapter 18. The key idea is the "probability histogram"—a graph which represents chance by area. These histograms are drawn *deus ex machina*, by the computer. However, we find graphs easier to use in the classroom than hypothetical lists of all possible samples. (The sample space representation appears as a technical note on p. 414; some instructors prefer this approach: our advice would be to do it in the context of quantitative data.) Probability histograms are introduced in figures 1 and 2, as the limit of empirical histograms from simulations. The reason for thinking about products (figure 2) is to see that not everything is normally distributed. The normal curve is tied to sums. Students should work exercise set A to pin down the interpretation of probability histograms.

Sections 3–4–5 present a "local" version of the central limit theorem: the probability histogram for the sum of a large number of draws from a box will follow the normal curve very closely. However, as the chapter points out, if the distribution of tickets in the box is highly skewed, then many draws may be needed before the approximation takes hold. (This will cause some test anxiety—how can they tell when it is safe to use the curve?) The continuity correction is introduced in section 4, to estimate the chance that the sum will take a given value. The official name itself, "the continuity correction," appears in the text. The phrase is a bit intimidating, but we wanted students to be able to look it up in case of need, and we wanted them to have some way of packaging the idea. Similarly, we have—with a little publication anxiety—the phrase "central limit theorem."

Some instructors are troubled by the approach in chapter 18, because they want the "global" central limit theorem: a sum will be in an interval with probability close to the corresponding area under the normal curve. In our experience, students see that if the probability histogram for the sum is close to the curve, areas under the histogram—probabilities—must be close to areas under the curve. The local theorem does imply the global one, both intuitively and formally.

With our approach, probability histograms have to be put into standard units before matching them to the normal curve: that is because we only have one normal curve—with mean 0 and SD 1. The scaling is done in figure 3 on p. 315, which is like figure 2 in chapter 5. The elided difficulty is non-trivial: Is the density of $a + bX$ equal to $\frac{1}{b} f(\frac{x-a}{b})$? or is it $bf(a+bx)$? Scaling is our substitute for the equation

$$P\{S_n < x\} = P\left\{\frac{S_n - n\mu}{\sigma\sqrt{n}} < \frac{x - n\mu}{\sigma\sqrt{n}}\right\}.$$

(See note 8 to the chapter.) In our experience, the equation is a loser; scaling works.

Note on the SD. The normal approximation shows why the SD is so useful. The shape of the probability histogram for the sum of a large number of draws from a box depends only on the average and SD of the numbers in the box. Other measures of spread, like average absolute deviation from average, have very little to do with it. (See note 9 to the chapter.)

Notes on review exercises. Exercise 3 tries to reinforce the idea that the histogram gives the exact answer, and the normal curve is just an approximation. Since the probability histogram is a difficult idea, students will confuse it with the histogram for the data—the draws from the box. Exercise 4 is on the continuity correction. Many students will be confused by the "and"; others will want to use the box $\boxed{13\ 0\text{'s}\quad 12\ 1\text{'s}}$, a confusion that may resurface in parts VI–VIII. Distinguishing between the data and the model is not so easy; exercise 5 may help. Exercise 6 previews hypothesis testing. Exercises 9 and 10 are about the number of draws needed for the central limit theorem to take over. (Also see exercises 5 and 6 on p. 324; the best thing for the students is to look at some pictures.) Exercise 11 reviews observed values, and #15 previews significance testing.

Part VI. Sampling

Chapter 19. Sample Surveys

There are a lot of ideas about sampling which are obvious to statisticians but not to others, and are well worth teaching in an elementary course. For example:

- The method used to draw the sample matters.
- Some methods are terrible.
- Handpicking the sample to get a representative cross-section tends not to work very well.
- Haphazard selection may be even worse.
- The best methods for drawing a sample involve the planned introduction of chance.
- If the non-response rate is high, the results may not be trustworthy.

Jumping straight into the calculations prevents the students from coming to grips with the basic ideas. That is why chapter 19 opens with a qualitative discussion, pinned to historical examples like the *Literary Digest* poll's choice of Landon (section 2), and the Gallup poll's "election" of Dewey (section 3). Probability methods are discussed in section 4, and their success is documented in section 5.

Elementary books (ours is no exception) concentrate on simple random sampling. Of course, the technical meaning of "random" is quite a bit more specialized than the usual meaning:

"Without definite aim, direction, rule, or method."

—Webster's

An effort is required to make students appreciate the technical meaning of "random." We take our best shot in sections 19.4 and 20.1; also see the discussion of "convenience samples" in section 23.4. Review exercise 6 on p. 352 may reinforce the point.

Once they know what the terms mean, students think that with a simple random sample, the sample percentage is very likely to equal the population percentage. (They are capable of thinking so, yet going on to compute 95% confidence intervals in response to word problems.) Chapter 16 was designed to prevent this confusion, and section 19.8 continues the work. Again, the chance-error language creates the image of the sample percentage coming close to the population percentage, but missing by a little:

sample percentage = population percentage + chance error.

(There is no bias term with simple random sampling.)

Real sample surveys, of course, use methods much more complicated than simple random sampling. Our book faces up to this issue. *Multistage cluster sampling* is introduced in section 4; it will be discussed again in chapter 22. Section 6 points to some of the difficulties faced by the Gallup poll, and section 7 discusses telephone surveys. Some of our teaching assistants confuse quota sampling with stratified sampling, and then wonder why we are attacking stratification. We aren't. The two methods are very different, although they start out the same way. The crucial difference is that with quota sampling, the interviewer is free to choose respondents to make up the quota. For a stratified sample, the choice of sampling units within each stratum is done objectively, using chance.

Review exercises 10 and 11 are designed to ease the students into confidence intervals; but the connection may need to be pointed out—later. Review exercise 12 is about non-response bias; so is exercise 12 on p. 351. Students like chapter 19, and they have little trouble with the exercises. They do have trouble with the terminology: *sample percentage*, *population*, *population percentage*, and *parameter* are all a bit remote.

Chapter 20. Chance Errors in Sampling

Section 20.1 reviews the definition of simple random sampling, and drives home the idea that the sample percentage will differ from the population percentage. Section 20.2 presents our version of $\sqrt{pq/n}$, except that the formula doesn't appear. (Well, it does, but only in a technical note on p. 362.) This may seem a bit idiosyncratic, and we would like to explain why we moved from the conventional formula to our version.

The students seemed to find $\sqrt{pq}$ rather hard to swallow. So we taught them to make a model with 0's and 1's in the box. Since we were working in percents, the formula became

$$\frac{\text{SD of 0--1 box}}{\sqrt{n}} \times 100\%.$$

We presented it that way for several years, but there was still a hitch. The students were willing to compute an SE as $\text{SD} \times \sqrt{n}$ in part V. When they hit part VI, there was a tremendous shifting of gears needed to compute the SE as $\text{SD}/\sqrt{n}$. Once they changed over, they stopped being able to compute the SE for a sum as $\text{SD} \times \sqrt{n}$—they insisted on dividing. We tried hard to explain that there was one formula to use with sums and another for averages, but they wouldn't buy it.

Eventually, we decided to have only one formula: the SE for a sum. Everything else is worked out from that. For instance, section 2 gives an example where 400 people are chosen at random from a population consisting of 3091 men and 3581 women; the problem is to compute the SE for the percentage of men in the sample. When presenting this problem in a lecture, we begin by writing on the blackboard:

Percent of men in sample will be around _____ give or take _____ or so.

Then we proceed as follows:

Step 1. Set up a box. First we write an empty box on the board:

We ask how many tickets there should be in the box. (Many students will answer 400.) Eventually, we arrive at

3581 ⬚0⬚ 's   3091 ⬚1⬚ 's

The number of men in the sample is like the sum of 400 draws from this box.

The last is a key sentence: it connects the box to the problem. (If students can be persuaded to write this sort of sentence on homework or tests, they will be in relatively good shape; also see exercise 1 on p. 391.)

Step 2. Now the calculation can be made:

$$\text{expected value for sum of 400 draws} = 400 \times \text{average of box}$$
$$= 400 \times 0.46 = 184.$$
$$\text{SE for sum of 400 draws} = \sqrt{400} \times \text{SD of box}$$
$$= \sqrt{400} \times \sqrt{0.46 \times 0.54}$$
$$\approx 20 \times 0.5 = 10.$$

We pause to interpret the results: the number of men in the sample will be around 184, give or take 10 or so.

Step 3. Convert to percent: 184 out of 400 is 46%, and 10 out of 400 is 2.5%. So the percentage of men in the sample will be around 46%, give or take 2.5% or so.

This works reasonably well for many students. Others will just compute "the SE" using a formula, and have one chance in four of picking the right formula out of the tool box. There are some exercises to discourage random formulas, for instance, numbers 3 and 5 on p. 361. Exercise 7 on p. 362 brings back the SE for the sum of quantitative variables.

Students have a hard time connecting the normal approximation for percentages with the mathematics in chapter 18—percentages look quite different from numbers. Figure 3 on p. 365 tries to make the connection, and seems to work reasonably well. (Also see figure 1 on p. 411.)

So far, we have been a bit sloppy about whether the draws are to be made with or without replacement. When the sample is only a small part of the population, it makes little difference. Section 4 discusses this issue, and eventually comes up with the correction factor

$$\sqrt{\frac{\text{number of tickets in the box} - \text{number of draws}}{\text{number of tickets in the box} - \text{one}}}.$$

In our opinion, this formula is somewhat technical for elementary students, and pushing it too hard obscures the really interesting point. When estimating percentages, accuracy depends mainly on the absolute size of the sample, rather than size relative to the population. On the other hand, when estimating numbers, the game changes (see, e.g., note 5 to the chapter).

Notes on review exercises. Exercise 1 covers the procedure for calculating the SE for a percentage, connecting it to the SE for a number. Exercise 2 puts in a plug for box models. Exercises 5 and 12 require computing the SE for a sum. Likewise, exercises 9–11 are about numbers. (Such exercises help to prevent the students from forgetting about part V.) Exercise 6 tests the point that accuracy depends mainly on the absolute size of the sample rather than the relative size.

Chapter 21. The Accuracy of Percentages

This chapter contains the first technical treatment of inference from the sample to the population. Section 1 states the question to be answered: how accurate is an estimated percentage likely to be? (Before that, however, the section reminds the student of the basic problem—the estimate is apt to be a bit off.) The chapter explains the answer: (i) accuracy is determined by the SE; (ii) the estimate is likely to be about right, but off by an SE or so.

The procedure for estimating the standard error from the sample—substitution of estimates for parameters in the formula— is called "the bootstrap method." (In our context, the procedure does happen to be a special case of the bootstrap; the samples are large, so the bootstrap works like a charm.) Many students will have trouble, because they do not distinguish between what is known and what is unknown. The point is somewhat delicate. After all, there is a substantial shift from the last chapter to this one. For instance, suppose there is a town with 10,000 residents of voting age and unknown political preferences. To estimate the percentage of Democrats in the town, a simple random sample of size 100 will be used. Consider two strategies:

- Determine the political leanings of every one of these 10,000 people, draw 100 at random and take the percentage of Democrats in the sample.
- Draw 100 at random, determine their political leanings and take the percentage of Democrats in the sample.

The first is zany, the second very practical. The usual standard-error calculation is made by thinking about the first process, the result being carried over to the second. Mathematically, that is fine—the probability distribution for the sample percentage of Democrats is the same in both setups. Students may feel the jolt.

We confront the distinction between the known and the unknown, at least to some degree (pp. 377–79 and 416). We even have some exercises where the students have to say what is given exactly and what must be estimated from the sample: see, for instance, exercise 1 on p. 379, exercise 9 on p. 380, or exercise 1 on p. 383. The distinction between "observed" and "expected" values comes in handy at this point.

Next, we discuss some problems in teaching the main worked example in the section (p. 378). The example is repeated here for ease of reference.

Example 1. In fall 2005, a city university had 25,000 registered students. To estimate the percentage who were living at home, a simple random sample of 400 students was drawn. It turned out that 317 of them were living at home. Estimate the percentage of students at the university who were living at home in fall 2005. Attach a standard error to the estimate.

In working such examples, teaching assistants often demonstrate a natural desire for mathematical efficiency:

$$\frac{\sqrt{400} \times \sqrt{0.79 \times 0.21}}{400} \times 100\% \approx 2\%.$$

We resist, because the parts lose their meaning for the students.

- $\sqrt{0.79 \times 0.21} \approx 0.41$ is the SD of the box, estimated by the bootstrap procedure.

- $\sqrt{400} \times 0.41 \approx 8$ is the SE for the number of students living at home. There were 317 such students in the sample, and the 8 measures the likely size of the chance error in the 317.
- $\frac{8}{400} \times 100\%$ is the SE for the percentage.

Truth to tell, we sometimes dodge the last step by saying, "8 out of 400 is 2 out of 100, or 2%." The idea is to keep the interpretation as rates, rather than letting percents disappear into ritual formalism.

This chapter makes the transition from probability calculations to statistical inference, and here is one consequence. Students will not take us seriously if we tell them, in working the example, "the sample number will be around its expected value give or take an SE or so." After all, the sample number is right there in front of them—it *is* 317. But the 317 is a little shaky, being based on a sample; the 8 tells us how shaky: and that is how we interpret the SE.

After dealing with standard errors, the chapter explains how to get confidence intervals for the population percentage at the 68%, 95%, and 99.7% levels by going 1, 2, or 3 SEs either way from the sample percentage. (The distinction between 1.96 SEs and 2 SEs, for instance, just didn't seem worth pursuing—among other things, the normal approximation may not be right to 3 decimal places.)

The conventional frequency interpretation for confidence intervals is given in section 3. (Bayesian colleagues are asked to temper justice with mercy.) Even for a hard-bitten frequentist, this is a difficult passage to teach, because many students will want to say,

> There is a 95% chance that the percentage of Democrats in the town is between. . . .

This is a natural human hope and we try not to deal with it too harshly. The section explains that the chance variability is in the sampling process not in the parameter. Exercises 1 and 2 on p. 386 reinforce the frequentist interpretation. Exercises 4–7 on pp. 386–87 are useful, but students may find the distinctions somewhat irritating.

Unfortunately, students find confidence intervals quite hard. In struggling with the complications, they are likely to lose track of the main point. So the section restates it, on p. 386: the SE tells you the likely size of the amount off. From our perspective, there is nothing wrong with omitting confidence intervals, and focusing on the SE as a measure of reliability. Just be careful about homework assignments.

As mentioned before, the Gallup poll uses a complex multistage cluster sample, and $\sqrt{pq/n}$ does not apply. This is hard. Students want to analyze the data, which is right there in front of them. They do not want to pay attention to the process generating the data, which is more remote. The point is tackled in section 4; also see exercise sets D and E. Many elementary statistics books do not face up to the issue, and perhaps that is one reason why investigators run around computing $\sqrt{pq/n}$ in situations where the results make little sense.

Notes on terminology. (i) We could not write the chapter without using the sample percentage-population percentage terminology, which is confusing to some students. The percentage of Democrats in the sample and the percentage of Democrats in the town are much more tangible, and the students pick up the idea through the examples. (ii) We try to distinguish between the "true" standard error computed from the box, and the standard error estimated from the sample. The latter is a "standard error of estimate," but this terminological elaboration would be too confusing. (Our use of SE rather than SD for random quantities is consistent with the standard-error-of-estimate language.)

Notes on review exercises. Exercises 1–2 cover the basics. Exercise 3 reminds the students that confidence intervals depend on the normal approximation (and see 3–4 in exercise set B on p. 383). Review exercises 7 and 9 are meant to teach the students not to use the standard error formula where it does not apply. Number 8 tries to block a purely syntactic approach—answering questions on the basis of key words or phrases, or even layout. Exercise 10 on sums is designed to review techniques from part V, and keep quantitative variables alive. Exercise 13 distinguishes between the histogram for the data and the probability histogram. Exercise 14 makes the point that the expected value and standard error depend on the box, not on the draws. Exercise 15 distinguishes what is known from what is estimated, in the sampling context. Some exercises are worded to suggest that calculations may not be feasible; students will find this disturbing, but the idea is an important one.

Chapter 22. Measuring Employment and Unemployment

Government estimates for the unemployment rate are prepared from the monthly Current Population Survey. This sample survey is discussed from the ground up. Such detail is unusual in an elementary text, but it consolidates the understanding of the material presented in the previous chapters, and gives the students a flying start on understanding any other large-scale survey. We don't test the students on details of the design. Mainly, we want them to learn that real surveys do not use simple random samples, so $\sqrt{pq/n}$ does not apply. The standard errors have to be estimated differently, and the half-sample method is sketched in section 5. One conclusion is that the calculation for the standard error should depend on the sample design. If the design is unknown, or poorly defined, sensible calculations are hard to make.

Many professionals are surprised to find that the complex design used by the Current Population Survey gives somewhat less accuracy than a simple random sample. Although the stratification and the ratio estimation reduce sampling error, the clustering increases it (p. 402). Of course, without the clustering nobody could afford to do the Survey. The real surprise, to us, is that the Current Population Survey is almost as accurate as a simple random sample. In complex designs, the effective sample size is often reduced by 15% to 50%. The Current Population Survey design is amazingly effective. Other statisticians ask why the ratio estimates are practically unbiased. Our explanation: the sample is very large, so the SEs are rather small, and the ratio estimates are almost linear in the data.

Notes on review exercises. Exercise 1(a) tests understanding of ratio estimates (section 4); part (b) does labor force definitions (section 3). Exercises 2–3–4 are about the half-sample method (section 5). Exercises 5 and 6 review definitions from chapter 19. Exercise 6 also makes the point that the SE depends on the sampling method. Exercises 7 and 8 test the understanding of probability samples. Exercise 9 is about interviewer bias (chapter 19). Exercise 11 tries to stop the parameter from being the random variable, after the sample is drawn. (Bayesians are permitted a wry chuckle.) Exercise 12 makes the point that confidence levels depend on the normal approximation, which will break down if the distribution is sufficiently skewed.

Chapter 23. The Accuracy of Averages

Section 1 explains how to calculate the standard error for the average of draws made at random with replacement from a box, by working back to the sum (p. 410 of the text). The interpretation is that the average of the draws will be around the average of the box, give or take an SE or so. Students handle this reasonably well, although by force of habit a few will go

SE for average of draws = (SE for sum/number of draws) × 100%.

Others will want to use the SE for the sum, with little sense that the order of magnitude is wrong. The formula "$\sigma/\sqrt{n}$" appears only in the technical note on p. 415 of the text; we do not teach it for reasons given earlier (pp. 27 of this manual).

The application to inference is in section 2. With a simple random sample, the SE of the average is estimated by substituting the SD of the sample for the unknown SD of the box. Then, confidence intervals are obtained by going the right number of SEs either way from the average of the sample. (In this chapter, the samples are large: small samples are dealt with, by Student's t, in chapter 26.)

At this point, to mix a metaphor, a lot of very tough chickens may come home to roost. Many students are going (somehow) to want 0–1 boxes in section 2. Others will want to use the SE for the sum rather than the SE for the average. Survivors will mix up the probability histogram for the average of the sample with a histogram for the data. Another confusion is between the SD of the sample and the SE of the average, so confidence intervals get interpreted as follows:

95% of the population is within 2 SEs of the average of the sample.

Some students fly over chapter 18, because they see no new techniques presented there. But in chapter 23, they have to come to grips with the central limit theorem. After all, how does the normal curve fit into a problem on educational levels, if the data are so far from normal? Figure 1 on p. 411 tries to explain why the probability histogram for the average of the draws follows the normal curve, making the connection to chapter 18 via the obvious (to us but not to them) change of scale.

The ideas in section 2 have all been introduced before, but they are difficult, and they interact in funny ways. Many students profit from studying figures 1 and 2. Others get things under control by working exercise set B. Section 3—and exercise set C—will also help: this exercise set reviews the mechanics and tests the distinctions between what is estimated and what is known. Exercise 4 in set C may seem primitive, but it forces the students to confront the concepts and pay attention to the scale of a histogram. Despite our best efforts, many students see no relationship among the SEs for sums, averages, numbers, and percents. Section 3 tries once again for unity.

As discussed earlier, the standard-error calculations presuppose simple random sampling, and the students are reminded of this in section 4. The calculations for confidence levels also depend on the normal approximation. Exercises 2–3 in set D (p.425) make the point. Exercises 4 and 6 reinforce the lesson that the SE depends on the design of the sample—and the SD.

Note on terminology. Students seem to find "sample average" a bit confusing: is it a sample of averages, or what? "The average of the sample" is better, and "the average of the draws" better yet. "Population" also tends to throw things off course. We find ourselves talking about "the box," and being understood better.

Notes on review exercises. These exercises force the students to distinguish between the SE and the SD. They also make the students separate out the histogram for the sample and the probability histogram for the average of the sample. They teach that the calculations depend on the normal approximation, and on simple random sampling. So they are tough, but provide good diagnostics.

The special review exercises cover parts I–VI. We comment on some of the problems. Numbers 3 and 4 review some issues in study design, and try to sharpen the understanding of confounders. The material on handedness came up in special review exercise 10, chapter 6. The twist here is using average age at death. As epidemiologists know, average age at death is a rather tricky statistic. Exercise 4 is designed to bring out the difficulty.

Exercise 5 is on the mean vs. the median. Exercise 8 reverses number 2 on p.174, defending against the syntactic approach. Exercise 10 reviews material from chapter 11, and tries to sharpen the connection between inequalities and regions in the scatter diagram. Exercise 11 is another version of 9–10 in chapter 12.

Exercises 13–15 cover part IV. Exercise 16 tries to separate the law of the averages from de Méré's paradox. Exercise 17 is a hard modeling question. Exercise 22 recaps observed values. Exercise 23 makes them squint at histograms, to see the connection between sums and averages. Exercise 25 is on selection bias. Exercise 27 tests to see if they know what confidence intervals are for. Exercise 28 has some interesting data, and tests the idea of cluster samples. Exercise 30, with random digit dialling, is the flip side of number 6 on p.372.

Exercise 19—an oldie-but-goodie—reviews probability histograms. There are two stumbling blocks:

(i) seeing that the number of heads when 100 coins are tossed is like the number of heads when one coin is tossed 100 times;

(ii) separating repetitions of tossing the coin within the group of 100 from repetitions of tossing the whole group.

The figure on the next page may help.

Special review exercise 23.19. A group of 100 coins are tossed over and over again. The top panel shows data on the number of heads with 100 repetitions, i.e., $100 \times 100 = 10,000$ individual tosses. The second panel is for 1000 repetitions, i.e., $1000 \times 100 = 100,000$ tosses; the third, for 10,000 repetitions, i.e., $10,000 \times 100 = 1,000,000$ tosses. The bottom panel is the probability histogram.

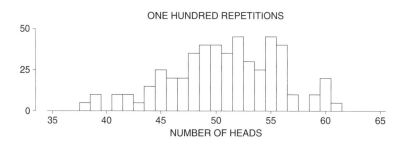

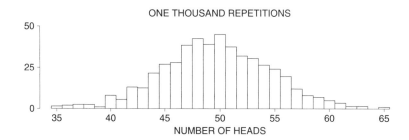

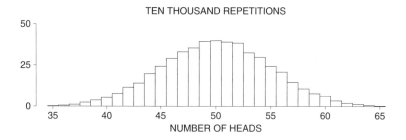

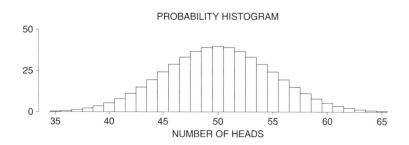

Part VII. Chance Models

In part VII, box models are used to study two topics: measurement error (chapter 24) and genetics (chapter 25). These topics are a bit unusual for an elementary statistics course; instructors who wish to skip them will find that part VIII was written with this possibility in mind. Part VII is designed to reinforce the lesson that to make a good statistical inference, the investigator has to get the box model right.[1]

Chapter 24. A Model for Measurement Error

With a large number of measurements, the standard error for the average is estimated as in chapter 23. You start by finding the SE for the sum of the measurements—

$$\sqrt{\text{number of measurements}} \times \text{SD}.$$

Then, you divide by the number of measurements, to get from the sum to the average. As in the sampling context, there is room for confusion between the SE and the SD. The discussion on pp. 442–43 (and the cartoon) try to separate these two quantities.

Despite the familiarity of the arithmetic, there is an issue in this chapter, and it is dealt with in sections 2–3. The procedure for computing the standard error is based on the square root law. The justification depends on viewing the measurements as the observed values of a sequence of independent, identically distributed random variables.

In our experience, that formulation does not convey much to students. We state the idea this way: the data are like the results of drawing at random with replacement from a box of numbered tickets. In particular, if there is any trend or pattern in the data, the model does not apply (pp. 445–49). Dependence between the measurements also rules the model out. Students can use this principle as a heuristic, relying on the ordinary meaning of "dependence."

In many cases, the model fits measurement data rather badly. The investigator develops some notion of what the next measurement "ought" to be, based on the previous data, and tends to report this notion instead of the real measurement, destroying the independence. That kind of observer bias is eliminated by the weighing design used at the National Bureau of Standards. See note 8 to the chapter.

Usually, one objective of measurement error models is to make a clean separation between the parameter being estimated (the "exact value" of the thing being measured) and the chance errors. There is a practical reason for this separation. For example, if repeated measurements are made by a certain process on a check weight, the variability in the results can be used to judge the likely size of the chance error in a measurement on another weight (example 5 on p. 451).

We set the model up with this in mind. There is a box of tickets, called the *error box*. Each ticket in the box represents a possible chance error, and the average

---

[1] Box models look special, because the draws (when made with replacement) are independent. However, the boxes can be modified to handle dependence. Just for one example, a pair of dependent random variables can be modeled by drawing at random from a box of tickets, where each ticket shows a pair of numbers (chapter 27).

of the numbers in the box is assumed to be 0. Then, each measurement equals the
exact value of the thing being measured, plus a draw with replacement from the box.
This is the Gauss model for measurement error. (The name should not be taken to
imply that the errors follow the normal curve.) In our somewhat primitive notation,
the model looks like this:

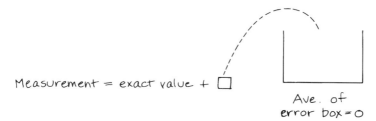

$$\text{Measurement} = \text{exact value} + \Box$$

Ave. of
error box = 0

More conventionally, the model would be stated as follows:

$$X_i = \mu + \epsilon_i$$

where the ϵ_i are independent, identically distributed, and have expectation 0.

   The model is explained in section 3, and the procedure for calculating the SE
is derived from the model. Bias—often a major problem—is taken up at the end of
the section. (Up to this point, bias has been assumed to be negligible.) The role of
the model in making inferences is summarized in section 4.

   Notes on review exercises. Parts (a–b) of exercise 1 are the basic blurts; parts
(c–f) try to ward off various misinterpretations of confidence intervals; part (f) is
hard. Exercise 2 tries to isolate the role of the normal curve; also see exercise 10.
Exercise 6 is about the role of the model. Exercises 8 and 9 bring the SE for the
sum back into play; of course, for the students, the first issue is to see that sums are
involved.

Chapter 25. Chance Models in Genetics

   This chapter gives a brief account of Mendel's genetic theory, based on his
experiments with peas. For statisticians, there is an interesting twist to the story:
Fisher argued that Mendel's data were massaged to make the frequencies closer to
their expected values (section 2). The geneticists do not agree, see note 7 to the
chapter. Fisher also showed that Galton's law of regression could be explained by
Mendelian theory. One version of the argument is presented in section 3, but it is
out of reach for most students.

   The physical source of the randomness in Mendelian genetics is described in
section 4. This is a tough story, but worth telling. One of the great strengths of the
model is the precise description of the physical sources of randomness. As we say
in the text, this chapter is included for two reasons:

   • Mendel's theory of genetics is beautiful science.
   • The theory shows the power of simple chance models in action.

Part VIII. Tests of significance

Chapter 26. Tests of Significance

The basic idea of the z-test is easy. If an observed value is too many SEs away from its expected value, something is wrong. But students find the vocabulary bewildering, and the implicit double negative is hard to follow: investigators usually proceed by rejecting the opposite of what they want to prove. Our objective was to teach the basic idea, and some of the conventional language—null hypothesis, test statistic, P-value. A more reasonable objective, perhaps, is just to teach the idea and skip the language. (Section 26.1 is organized with this possibility in mind.)

We decided to focus on one test first, developing the ideas and the language in that case, and only then moving on to other tests. We chose to start with the z-test. One-tailed tests are used throughout this chapter and the next, as students find them more natural than the two-tailed variety. (There are enough other complications to justify postponing this one to section 29.2.)

Section 1 introduces the idea of the z-test. In the example, the null hypothesis says that the average of the box is 50. The alternative hypothesis says that the average of the box is less than 50. There is a difference between the observed sample average of 48 and the expected value of 50. The null hypothesis interprets this difference as chance variation. The alternative says the difference is real, i.e., reflects a fact about the box.

Section 2 recommends that you set up the null and alternative hypotheses as statements about a box. Few students will pay attention to this advice, but it is the key to all that follows. As we see it, a box model is needed to make the z-test, because the model is what defines the chances. This argument is taken up again in chapter 29.

Section 3 introduces the *test statistic z* and the *observed significance level* or *P-value*:

$$z = \frac{\text{observed} - \text{expected}}{\text{SE}} \quad , \qquad P \approx \text{(shaded area under normal curve to left of } z \text{)}$$

When the P-value of a test is very small, we tend to quote it as a fraction rather than a percent (p.479). Some students will need help in seeing the connection.

The conventional frequentist interpretation of P is given (apologies to our Bayesian colleagues). If the null hypothesis is right, and the experiment is repeated many times, then P is the proportion of repetitions giving z's more extreme than the observed one. The students are then taught that a test of significance is an argument by contradiction (not an easy pitch to make, because many of them don't know what an argument by contradiction is). Exercises 4–5 in set D try to help with the frequentist interpretation of P.

Section 4 reviews the steps involved in making a test, and introduces the 5% and 1% levels. As we tell the students, a result is *significant* if P is less than 5%, *highly significant* if P is less than 1%. (However, we suggest reporting P instead of just saying how it compares to 5% and 1%.) Many students jump to the conclusion that P represents the chance of the null hypothesis being true. Measures are taken to prevent this mistake, in the text, in exercise 2 on p. 481, and in other exercises. Some students will need to be told, more than once, that small P is bad for the null, big P is good for the null (e.g., exercise 2 on p. 482).

Section 5 shows how to make the z-test for qualitative data. The lead example is an ESP experiment done by Charles Tart at U.C. Davis. In this example, and many others, we think there is no natural alternative hypothesis about the box. If a subject has ESP, there is no reason to suppose the successive guesses are independent, so $p > 1/2$ isn't a plausible hypothesis—there is no p. After the first edition of *Statistics* was published, Tart tried to replicate his ESP experiment, but found no effect—section 29.5. (This is association not causation.) He explained the failure to replicate by a change in student attitudes: "In the last year or two, students have become more serious, competitive and achievement-oriented. . . ."

Exercises 1–5 in set E (pp. 486ff) go through testing, step by step. Number 9 reinforces the point that the argument is about the box (i.e., the parameters in the model) not the sample. Also see exercise 4 on p. 478. Exercise 11 does the sign test. Exercise 10 is interesting, and there are two ways for students to go off the rails:

    (i)   using the sample SD instead of the population SD, and
    (ii) making a two-sample test, using the two SDs.

Instructors will get to see the second mistake only by having the exercise on a quiz, after doing chapter 27.

Our version of the z-statistic is

$$z = \frac{\text{observed} - \text{expected}}{\text{SE}}.$$

Many students find this equation a bit cryptic, and do not see how get started using it. We ask, "Well, what is observed?" If the observed value is an average, for example, then they need the expected value for the average, i.e., the average of the box—and the SE for the average of the draws. The discussion on p. 485 may help. We motivate the equation this way: z puts the observed value into standard units.

Section 6 does the t-test. We consider this to be a fairly technical topic for an introductory course, and skip it when pressed for time.

Notes on review exercises. The exercises are designed to emphasize the logical steps involved in making a z-test: formulating hypotheses as statements about a box model, then computing z and P. In many of the exercises—for instance, numbers 8 or 10—students will have a very hard time setting up the box model. (The issue for them in working #8 is choosing the right SD.) Exercise 11 boils down to testing whether a coin is fair or biased. Exercise 12 explains methods for handling paired data (the sign test, the z-test on differences).

Note on coverage. We do not introduce the terms *size* or *level*, or use the symbol α. The concept of *power* is not introduced: there is enough to do as it is. The connection between tests and confidence intervals is not established: students rarely see the point of isomorphisms.

Chapter 27. More Tests for Averages

Section 1 explains how to calculate the standard error for the difference of two independent chance quantities. Example 2 and exercises in set A stress the assumption of independence. Section 2 presents the two-sample z-test. The context is the decrease in reading scores over the period 1990–2004, as measured by NAEP (National Assessment of Educational Progress). The section shows how to set up the model, with two boxes. Another example does the 0–1 coding. Our test statistic is the standard one, in disguise (note 3 to the chapter). Some students will get lost in scaling. For instance, they will figure the difference in percentage points, but its SE in decimals. Exercise 5 on p. 507 helps. Ideally, of course, each SE should be seen as the margin of error in some estimate.

Section 3 applies the two-sample z-test to experimental data. We set up the model with two possible responses for each subject. One is observed if you put the subject into the treatment group, the other if you put the subject into the control group. But you cannot observe both. Suppose there are N subjects: n are chosen at random for the treatment group, and m for the control group, with $n + m \leq N$. If $n + m$ is much smaller than N, there are in effect two separate boxes, and the theory of section 27.1 applies directly (for a real example, see review exercise 8). Now there is a glitch. If $n + m$ is comparable to N—and $n + m = N$ is the usual case in clinical trials—the treatment and control averages are dependent. Furthermore, the difference between drawing with or without replacement matters. In principle, then, it is wrong to model the data as two independent samples drawn from two large boxes. Fortunately or otherwise, this fine point has no practical consequences. Ordinarily, treating the two samples as independent and drawn with replacement will give an excellent approximation to the SE for the difference between the averages. (For discussion, see notes 11 and 14 to the chapter, which also provide a brief review of the literature on the model.)

In example 4 on p.508, the calculation is made blindly. The logic is discussed afterward, on pp.509–10. This is a difficult passage. Students have to work hard to see that the sample averages are dependent. Some of them will be irritated to find that the dependence does not matter—for reasons which may also seem mysterious. Section 4 presents a real example with qualitative data—an experimental test of "rational" decision theory. Exercise 3 on p.515 does some calculations for the HIP trial on mammography (pp.22–23), and points to a design issue. Breast cancer is a rare disease. Even if screening cuts the death rate from breast cancer in half, the impact on the total death rate is unlikely to achieve statistical significance—unless sample sizes are incredibly large. That is why investigators look at cause-specific mortality rates. Section 5 tries to explain when the z-test applies.

Notes on review exercises. The point of exercise 1 is to make the students distinguish between one-sample and two-sample tests. Exercises 2–3 are straightforward two-sample problems; number 2(b) hints that averages may have better power. In exercise 4, the test cannot be done—dependence (see exercises 5–6 on pp.515–16). Review exercises 5–7 are fairly straightforward experimental setups. Number 8, again on experiments, is much harder. Students either don't see what is being compared to what, or find the comparisons too unnatural to make. In grading this one, we insist on a substantive conclusion—for instance, that people are poor predictors of their own behavior, but tend to live up to their predictions about themselves—as one character in the drawing understands. Question 11 is very theoretical. The hope is to persuade at least some of the students that a significance test is not a ritual, but an argument that has is own internal logic.

"I'm not asking for a raise, Sir. I just want to know how you would react if I did."

Chapter 28. The Chi-Square Test

Section 1 presents the χ^2-test for goodness of fit, when the model is completely specified. Students have a hard time deciding when to use the χ^2-test and when to use the z-test; some help is given on p.523; also see exercises 3–6 on pp.539–40. The text explains how to read the χ^2-table (p.527), and says that the χ^2-distribution is only an approximation. The mathematical underpinnings for the approximation are discussed in section 1. The main one is a box model; this is emphasized in the text. Figure 2 (p.528) for 60 rolls may help. As the number of rolls goes up—60, 600, 6000—the probability histogram will get closer and closer to the smooth curve. The figure below plots the probability histogram for 600 rolls. The histogram is already very close to the curve.

Probability histogram for the null distribution of the χ^2-statistic in 600 rolls of a fair die. (Continues figure 2 in chapter 28.)

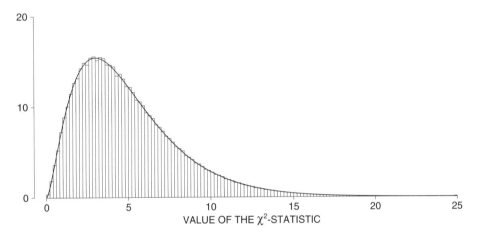

Section 1 closes with a real example—testing the wheel of fortune. Section 2 describes χ^2, in some degree of generality, as a goodness-of-fit test. Section 3 discusses the pooling of independent χ^2's, and shows how Fisher used the χ^2-test to check up on Mendel (but see note 7 to chapter 25, for the geneticists' counter-arguments). Fisher computed a left-hand tail area, rather than a right-hand tail (p.534). Students see a possible trap, so the issue will get air time. Section 4 shows how χ^2 is used to test for dependence in $m \times n$ tables. With the current exposition, this is fairly easy going.

Notes on review exercises. Exercise 1 confronts the issue of which test to use when. Exercises 2 and 7 are straightforward goodness-of-fit questions. Number 3 does independence in a 3×3 table, while number 9 does a 3×2 table. Exercises 4–5 are qualitative, and get the students to focus again on probability histograms and tail areas. Students may find exercise 6 a little ambiguous, but left-hand tail areas are called for. Exercise 10 is based on a court case—does the χ^2-test show discrimination in the criminal justice system of Northern Ireland? (In a law case, finding a mistake by an opposing expert is powerful—and guessing how the mistake was made is dynamite.)

Chapter 29. A Closer Look at Tests of Significance

Many people find tests of significance both complicated and mysterious. Perhaps as a result, the limitations of the technique are often ignored. This often creates unnecessary confusion. So we think it is important to discuss what tests of significance don't do. That is the topic of chapter 29.

Section 1 is about fixed-level testing (a procedure we do not recommend). Section 2 covers data snooping. Students find it very hard to understand that significance levels are compromised by multiple looks at the data. Exercise 5 on p. 483 and exercise 1 on p. 550 should help, a little; exercises 2–5 on pp. 551–52 give some practical examples. We see the "one-tail-or-two" issue as quite minor.[1] Many professionals will not agree with us, and the students like a definite rule for deciding whether to use a one-tailed or a two-tailed test (pp. 547–50). The issue will get some attention.

Section 3 tries to explain that small differences can be statistically significant—or big differences insignificant—depending on the sample size. This point is hard, and irritating. Students have invested a lot of time learning how to operate the tool, they want it to be useful. Section 4 is about the role of the model in testing. Since the arithmetic of the test seems to generate the chances—the P-value—this section is quite subtle. Section 5 stresses the role of design, and section 6 is a reminder about the basic question being addressed by significance tests: is the difference too large to explain by chance?

Notes on review exercises. Exercises 1 and 2 are straightforward questions, which can be answered from the reading. Exercise 3 is a math question but a little tricky, the point being that P-values depend on sample size. Exercise 4 is about data snooping, among other things; hard. Exercises 5 and 7 are about not doing tests when you have all the data, an idea the students pick up. Exercises 8–9 are on sample design, and are hard. Exercises 6 and 10 are about real studies and raise real questions; very hard.

Finally, we comment on some of the special review exercises, which cover the whole book. Exercises 1–2 are on study design. Exercise 3 covers Simpson's paradox. Exercise 4 makes the point that histograms are different from bar graphs (also see exercise 8 on pp. 52–53). Exercise 6 is on percentiles for skew distributions. Exercise 7 makes them look at scatter diagrams (to find the child brides and grooms at the lower left). Exercises 8–14 cover part III: number 8 involves a lot of work on a small data set. Exercise 9(a) does attenuation, while 9(b) covers ecological correlations. Exercise 10 is another variation on the regression effect. Exercise 11 involves percentile ranks, and will be quite a challenge. With exercise 14, students will have to work out a percentage from the normal approximation, then a number.

Exercises 15–17 cover parts IV and V. Exercise 15 requires careful reading; compare exercise 11 on p. 253. Exercise 16 looks like a binomial problem, but it isn't—they will need to think about the ideas in order to work the problem. Exercise 17 requires a box model; not completely transparent. Sampling is the next topic.

---

[1] The data-snooping that goes into developing a typical regression model seems much more serious; of course, the application to cholesterol is far from minor (example 2 on p. 550).

Number 18 is on selection bias; 19 is on evaluation of survey results. Exercise 21 puts reverse spin on #30, p.436. Exercise 22 combines ideas from sampling with the continuity correction. Exercise 23 examines some design issues in sampling. Students often make "cluster sample" mean any kind of sample they don't like, and we try to block that move. Exercises 25, 26, and 28 try to stop some misinterpretations of expected values and confidence levels; #28 is based on a court opinion which got the wrong answer. Exercise 31 is on measurement error, and 32 on genetics. Exercise 33 tries to make the students understand when to use a one-sample z-test or a two-sample test. Exercise 34 is to prevent misinterpretations of P. The data in exercise 36 are interesting, and the idea is not to make a two-sample z-test with correlated responses.

Answers to Review Exercises

Part I. Design of Experiments

Chapter 2. Observational Studies

1. (a) Too hasty. What about population size?

    Comments: Michigan may include the big bad city, but Minnesota has twice the population of Michigan. The crime rate is lower in Michigan. (Of course, there probably are neighborhoods in Detroit that are best avoided.)

   (b) This is better reasoning, because the population of the U.S. increased over the period 1991–2001. Looking at rates would make the point even more clearly. (In fact, there has been a remarkable decline in crime rates over the period 1980–2005.)

2. (a) What's missing is the number of cars on the road, and there were a lot more Corvettes. (For example, 33,586 Corvettes were sold in 2002, versus 8,065 Q45s.) You need to look at rates. If anything, thieves prefer the Q45—a much classier car.

   (b) Same issue as (a).

   (c) False. The rate is low because the denominator is large relative to the numerator. The rate compares the number of jeeps stolen to the number sold. That's the point of using a rate.

3. No. In the Salk trial, the parents who consented were on the whole better off than the parents who did not consent, and their children were more at risk to begin with (p. 4).

4. (a) They were controlling for age and sex as possible confounders; this is discussed on p. 13, with respect to a specific disease—lung cancer.

   (b) This is the wrong conclusion to draw. Ex-smokers are a self-selected group, and many people give up smoking because they are sick. So recent ex-smokers include a lot of sick people. (Other epidemiological data show that if you quit smoking, you will live longer.)

5. No. The data from the double-blind study are more reliable, and suggest that the results from the single-blind were biased.

6. Subjects who did not improve during the first part of the trial probably concluded that they were on the placebo (whether they were or they weren't) and would be switched to the "real" medication during the second part of the trial. This expectation made them improve—the placebo effect.

7. (a) This is an observational study, so confounding may be a problem.

    (b) Rates of cervical cancer go up with age. Women of different marital status have different patterns of sexual activity, and are therefore exposed to different kinds of risk; similarly for education. In other words, age, marital status, and education are potential confounders.

    (c) Pill users are more active sexually than non-users, and have more partners. That seems to be what makes the rate of cervical cancer higher among pill users. (This is like example 2 on p. 16 or exercise 11 on p. 23.)

    (d) No; see (c).

8. Memorial Day is at the end of May; Labor Day is early in September. Just over 25% of the days of the year fall in between. Even if burglars work the same amount every day, over 25% of the burglaries would occur between Memorial Day and Labor Day.

9. (a) False. (b) True. (c) False: that is the whole point of experiments.

    Discussion. People who eat lots of fruits and vegetables are different from the rest of us in many other ways. Some other aspect of diet or life style may be protective. Of course, the observational studies might be right; something in the fruits and vegetables other than the vitamins might be the protective factor.

10. (a) Observational study. (b) Yes. (c) Yes.

    (d) No. The gene would also have to be associated with controlling behavior by the mother (p. 20).

    (e) A mother who sees her child eat too much might respond in a way that psychologists would interpret as "controlling"—Johnny, stop eating!

    (f) No. The *Chronicle* seems to have over-reacted.

11. (a) The treatment group consists of those who finished boot camp. The control group consists of other prisoners—including those who do not volunteer, or those who volunteer but do not complete the program.

    (b) This is observational. The prisoners decide whether to volunteer for boot camp and whether to stay in the program or drop out. That is the problem: those who volunteer and stay the course might be quite different from who volunteer but drop out.

    (c) False.

    Comment. An experiment could be done either like the polio trial (p. 1ff) or the HIP trial (exercise 9 on pp. 22–23):

    Like the polio trial. Ask for volunteers. Randomize some of the volunteers to treatment (assignment to boot camp) and some to control. Compare the recidivism rate for the two groups—but include the dropouts in the treatment group. (Otherwise, you still have the problem of self-selection.)

Like the HIP trial. Take a group of prisoners. Randomize some to treatment (invitation to participate in boot camp) and some to control. Compare the recidivism rate for the two groups—but include in the treatment group those who decline to participate and those who drop out. (Again, this is to guard against the problem of self-selection.)

12. False. The conclusion does not follow. This is just like the admissions study (pp. 17ff). The Democrats may be concentrated in wards with low turnouts. Here is an example, with only two wards (and see exercise 13 on p. 24).

	DEMOCRATS		REPUBLICANS	
	Total number	Number voting	Total number	Number voting
Ward A	1000	100	100	5
Ward B	100	60	1000	500

Part II. Descriptive Statistics

Chapter 3. The Histogram

1. 66 inches, 72 inches.

2. (a) There are more at age 1. The histogram is higher at 1 than at 71.

   (b) There are more at age 21.

   (c) There are more age 0–4,

   (d) 50%

Histogram for review exercise 2, chapter 3

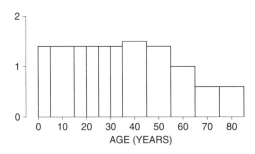

3. (a) Rounding.

   (b) No. Taking percentages adjusts for the difference between the total numbers. On the whole, rental units tend to be smaller.

   (c) Rental units are smaller, as noted above.

Histograms for review exercise 3, chapter 3
(The histogram for owners is shifted to the right)

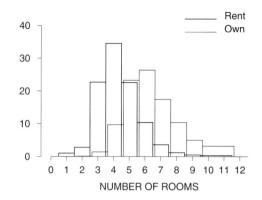

4. (a) 25% (b) 99% (c) 140–150 mm (d) 135–140 mm
   (e) About $5 \times 2.1 = 10.5\%$ (f) 102–103 mm
   (g) 117–118 mm is a good guess; the interval is somewhere between 115 and 120 mm.

5. $10 thousand $\times$ 1% per thousand dollars $= 10\%$.

6. (i) and (ii) not (iii).
   Reason: With lists (i) and (ii), 25% of the people have heights between 66.5 inches and 67.5 inches; 50% between 67.5 and 68.5 inches; 25% between 68.5 and 69.5 inches. Not so with list (iii).

7. (i) Natural causes. (ii) Trauma.
   Reason: Young people die of accidents, murder, etc. Old people die of heart disease, cancer, etc.

8. (a) is true, (b) and (c) are false. The figure does not adjust for the different lengths of the class intervals, and is misleading for that reason.

9. (a) True. (b) True.
   (c) People with failing GPAs may round them up; and 2 is such an important number—for GPAs—that people with GPAs just above 2 may round them down.

10. (a) The histogram is shown below.

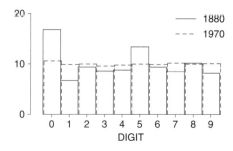

10. (b) In 1880, people did not know their ages at all accurately, and rounded off.

(c) In 1970, people knew when they were born.

(d) In 1880, there was a strong preference for even digits (although 4 and 6 lose out to 5); again, this is probably due to rounding. In 1970, the preference was much weaker.

11. The lowest of the top 15 scores is 90. Then there is a gap of 6 points—the next score is 84. There is no gap anything like this big in the rest of the distribution.

12. False. There are very few days where the temperature is above 90 degrees. The investigators should have looked at the number of riots divided by the number of days in each temperature range.

Chapter 4. The Average and the Standard Deviation

1. (a) Average = 50. Deviations = $-9, -2, 0, 0, 4, 7$. The SD is

$$\sqrt{\frac{(-9)^2 + (-2)^2 + 0^2 + 0^2 + 4^2 + 7^2}{6}} = 5.$$

(b) 48, 50, 50 are within 0.5 SDs of average, i.e., in the range from 47.5 to 52.5.

48, 50, 50, 54, 57 are within 1.5 SDs of average, i.e., in the range from 42.5 to 57.5.

2. (a) List (ii) has the smaller SD, because it has more entries at the average.

(b) This time, list (i) has the smaller SD: list (ii) has two wild entries, 1 and 99.

3. (a) 5. The average should be in the middle of the distribution: only three of the numbers are smaller than 1, and none are bigger than 10.

(b) 3. If the SD is 1, the entries 0.6 and 9.9 are much too far from average. The SD can't be 6, because none of the numbers are more than 6 away from the average.

4. For income, the average will be bigger than the median—long right hand tail at work (pp. 64–65). For education, the average will be smaller than the median: the histogram has a long left hand tail (p. 39).

5. 80 mm is more than 3 SDs below average, and is unusually low. 115 mm and 120 mm are about average. 210 mm is unusually high.

6. (a) (i) 60 (ii) 50 (iii) 40

(b) (i) median is bigger than the average—long left hand tail
    (ii) median is about equal to the average—symmetry
    (iii) median is less than the average—long right hand tail

(c) 15. Most of the area is within 50 of the average, so 50 is too big. Only a little of the area is within 5 of the average, so 5 is too small.

(d) False. Histograms (i) and (iii) are almost mirror images, and have just about the same SD.

TES TO REVIEW EXERCISES

7. (a) Average weight of men $= 66 \times 2.2 \approx 145$ pounds, SD ≈ 20 pounds.
    Average weight of women ≈ 121 pounds, SD ≈ 20 pounds.

    (b) 68%: the range is average ± 1 SD.

    (c) bigger than 9 kg: if you take the men and the women together, the spread
    in weights goes up.

8. (a) The girls have to be the same height (on average) as the boys at age 11.
    Otherwise, the average height of all the children would differ from the
    average of the boys.

    (b) $(137 + 151)/2 = 144$ cm.

9. (a) Yes: the average goes up by $(\$986{,}000 - \$98{,}600)/1000 = \$887.40$.

    (b) No. (That is one advantage of the median: it is not thrown off by outliers.)

10. (a) 163, the average.

    (b) \$8, because the SD is 8; see p. 68.

11. \$8, because the SD is 8, and the SD is the r.m.s. deviation from average.

12. The data are cross sectional not longitudinal, so the data only provide weak
    support for the theory. (Longitudinal data show that most spells of poverty are
    short; see the references in note 15 to chapter 4.)

Chapter 5. The Normal Approximation for Data

1. (a) 79% of $25 \approx 20$.

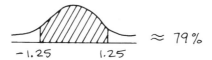

    (b) 18.

2. Something is wrong with the computer. The entries should be around 1 in size,
    but they are way too big. The first score, for example, is 6.2 SDs below average;
    the eighth score is even farther down.

    Comment for mathematicians. A list of 100 numbers cannot have an entry more
    than $\sqrt{99} \approx 10$ SDs away from average. *Sketch of proof.* (i) Standarize the list
    to have mean 0 and variance 1. (ii) If the largest entry is L, minimize the sum
    of squares of the other 99 entries, their sum being constrained to equal $-L$.

3. (a) In 1967, a score of 700 was 1.43 SDs above average: $(700 - 543)/110 \approx$
    1.43. The percentage scoring over 700 was about 8%—

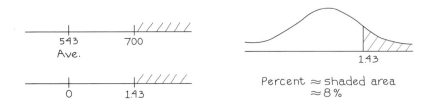

(b) In 1994, a score of 700 was 1.83 SDs above average, and the percentage scoring over 700 was about 3%.

4. (a) 9% (b) 5%

5. The percentage of men with heights between 66 inches and 72 inches is exactly equal to the area between 66 inches and 72 inches under the histogram. This percentage is approximately equal to the area between -1 and $+1$ under the normal curve.

6. No. For example, the normal curve says that about 16% of the scores should be more than 1 SD above average, and none are.

7. (a) 400 is 1.5 SDs below average; this student is in the 7th percentile of the score distribution (approximately), because the area to left of -1.5 under the normal curve is 7%.

   (b) The student needs to be about 0.7 SDs above average, so, needs a score of about 620 on the M-SAT. (The 75th percentile is nearly 0.675, rounded here to 0.7.)

8. (a) True. See pp. 92ff.

   (b) False: all the deviations from average stay the same.

   (c) True.

   (d) True: all the deviations from average are doubled.

   (e) True.

   (f) False: all the deviations from average have their signs changed, but that goes away in the squaring. The SD has to be positive (or, exceptionally, zero).

9. (a) False. For example, the list 1, 2, 99 has a median of 2 and an average of 34.

   (b) False. For the list 1, 2, 99, two-thirds of the entries are below average.

   (c) False. For example, income data (p. 88) have a long right-hand tail; educational levels have a long left-hand tail as well as bumps at 8, 12 and 16 years (p. 39).

   (d) False. If the histogram for a list follows the normal curve, the percentage of entries within 1 SD of average will be around 68%. Otherwise, the percentage could be a lot different. For instance, take a list of eight numbers: one is 30, one is 70, and six are 50. The average is 50, the SD is 10, and 75% are within 1 SD of average.

10. The histogram has a long right hand tail, the median is well below average. Therefore, a lot less than 50% are earning above $32,000. Choose 40%.

11. Histogram (i) is right. With (ii), the average of 1.1 would be right in the middle, and a lot of people would be taking fewer than $1.1 - 1.5 = -0.4$ courses. Histogram (iii) is even worse.

12. The students who take the subject-matter tests are the ones applying to the better schools—and in general, these are the better students.

Chapter 6. Measurement Error

1. False: each measurement is thrown off by chance error, and this changes from measurement to measurement. (It is a good idea to replicate measurements, so as to judge the likely size of the chance error.)

2. (a) The tape may have stretched; the hook at the end may have moved.
   (b) Cloth.
   (c) Yes, as the tape stretches or the hook moves.

3. (a) False. Chance errors are sometimes positive and sometimes negative. Bias pushes in one direction.
   (b) False, same reason.
   (c) True.

4. 0.03 inches or so.

5. (a) No. Persons 2 and 10 copied from each other: they got exactly the same answers, with the decimal point in the wrong place. The other students probably worked independently.
   (b) First, nobody got the same answer both times. Second, there is a lot of person-to-person variation.

Chapter 6. Special Review Exercises

1. False; see p. 89.

2. (a) All the numbers on the list are the same. Example: 2, 2, 2.
   (b) All the numbers on the list are 0.

3. We can get the SD by looking at the first two scores, in original units and in standard units: $79 - 64 = 15$ points, while $1.8 - 0.8 = 1.0$. So, $1.0\,\text{SD} = 15$ points, and the SD is 15 points. Next, we get the average from the fact that 64 is 0.8 in standard units: $0.8\,\text{SD} = 12$ points, so the average must be $64 - 12 = 52$. Finally, we complete the table:

$$
\begin{array}{ccc}
52 & 72 & 31 \\
0 & 1.33 & -1.4
\end{array}
$$

4. (a) Approximately equal to the area under the curve between -1.5 and 1.5, or 87%.

(b) 560. The range 450–650 corresponds to ±1 in standard units. About 68% of the students at the university had scores in this range. There must have been about $1000/0.68 \approx 1470$ students at the university. The range 500–600 corresponds to ±0.5 in standard units. About 38% of the students at the university had scores in this range: 38% of $1470 = 0.38 \times 1470 \approx 560$. Moral: the normal curve is not a rectangle.

5. Probably a recording error was made at one interview or the other.

6. (a) $(600 + 650)/2 = 625$

   (b) More than 125. When you put the men and women together, the spread goes up, because the two distributions are different.

7. The average is 630; again, the SD is more than 125.

8. You would be too low, because the curve is lower than the histogram in that range.

9. Average $= 10 - 6.4 = 3.6$ and SD $= 2.0$.
   Reason: number wrong $= 10 -$ number right.

10. False. The data are cross sectional not longitudinal. The 20-year-olds were born 1956–60; the 70-year-olds, 1906–10. In the early part of the century, there was much more pressure to conform and be right-handed.

    Comment. Some investigators believe that left-handed people suffer higher mortality, and use the trend in left-handedness as supporting evidence. See Stanley Coren, "Left-handedness and accident-related injury risk" *American Journal of Public Health* vol. 79 (1989) pp. 1040–41, and "The diminished number of older left-handers: differential mortality or social-historical trend?" *International Journal of Neuroscience* vol. 75 (1994) pp. 1–8. However, Coren's argument seems a little shaky. For some evidence in the other direction, see M. E. Salive et al., "Left-handedness and mortality," *American Journal of Public Health* vol. 83 (1993) pp. 265–7.

11. By symmetry, the average is half way between the 25th and 75th percentiles, and is 64.0 inches. The 75th percentile is about 0.67 SDs above average, so, the SD is $(65.8 - 64.0)/0.675 \approx 2.7$ inches. The 90th percentile is about 1.28 SDs above average, that is, $64.0 + 1.28 \times 2.7 \approx 67.5$ inches.

12. The likely explanation is digit preference. People round their incomes to the nearest $1,000 or $10,000. The class interval $15,000–$17,500 includes the left endpoint (a beautiful round number) as well as $16,000 and $17,000. The next class interval, $17,500–$20,000, includes $18,000 and $19,000 but not $20,000: class intervals include left endpoints not right endpoints. So this second interval has only two round numbers in it, rather than three; neither is as round as $15,000. The other pairs of intervals are similar to these two. People with incomes below $15,000 seem less prone to rounding: every dollar counts.

13. (a) Heart disease rates go up with age: the drivers could be older, accounting for the difference in rates. That explanation has been eliminated.

(b) You want the difference in rates to be due to exercise on the job, rather than pre-existing factors. It might take some time for exercise to have its beneficial effect.

(c) Drivers and conductors are going to be similar with respect to age, education, income, and so forth.

(d) This is an observational study, so there may be some confounding. Drivers may be more at risk than conductors to start with. For example, drivers may be heavier.

(e) You could look to see if the drivers and conductors had similar body sizes when they were hired; that would suggest the two groups were comparable at time of hire, and strengthen the argument that exercise matters. If drivers were heavier than conductors at time of hire, the argument for exercise is weaker.

Comment. As it turned out, the drivers were heavier than the conductors at time of hire, explaining the difference in rates of heart disease.

14. Moving high-risk women from the control group to the treatment group lowers the death rate in the control group and increases the death rate in the treatment group. That biases the study against screening.

The assignment does increase the detection rate in the treatment group, but that is not how benefits are measured. The number of lives saved has to be determined by comparing the death rates in the treatment and control groups, and the bias runs against treatment. (Doctors can seldom tell what would have happened if a patient had chosen a different treatment: that is why clinical trials are needed.)

15. The experimental comparison is treatment (groups B + C) versus controls (group A). The investigator is making observational comparisons, because treatment cases select themselves into group B or C. Cases that opt for a pretrial conference are probably different from cases that don't—so there will be lots of confounding. Similar issues came up when comparing the consent and no-consent groups in the Salk vaccine field trial (section 1.1), the adherers and the non-adherers in the clofibrate trial (section 2.2), or the examined and refused groups in the HIP trial (exercise 9 on pp. 22–23). Furthermore, the investigator does not seem to be presenting all the data. For example, there were 2954 cases in all; only 2780 are reported in the first table. Also, 22% of 701 ≈ 154 of the group B cases reached trial (first table). The second table only reports on 63 cases in group B. There is a similar issue for groups A and C.

Part III. Correlation and Regression

Chapter 8. Correlation

1. The answer is (d). With (a), the averages are too low. With (b), the SDs are too small. With (c), the SDs are too big and the correlation is too high.

2. (a) Negative: older cars get fewer miles per gallon.

(b) Richer people own newer cars, and maintain them better. (Some rich people own Ferrari gas guzzlers, but not many; and 10-year-old Chevrolets in poor repair might guzzle even more.)

3. The correlation would be 1.00. All the points on the scatter diagram for height of wife vs. height of husband would lie on a straight line which slopes up. The slope of the line is 0.92, but correlation and slope are two different things.

4. 0.3. Taller men do marry taller women, on average. But there is lots of variation around the line.

5. (i) 0.60   (ii) 0.30   (iii) 0.95

   Reasoning: correlation (iii) must be nearly 1; correlations (i) and (ii) are moderate, with (i) being stronger.

6. This is false (p. 126).

7.
$$
\begin{array}{rr}
0.62 & -1.00 \\
-0.85 & 0.97 \\
0.06 & -0.38
\end{array}
$$

8. (a) 42 inches   (b) 2.5 inches   (c) 0.80   (d) solid

9. (a) -0.80 (b) 0.3   (c) 1.00

   Comment. In (c), all the points lie on the line $y = 2x$, so there is no need to do any arithmetic.

10. Smaller when the score on form L is 75. If you take narrow vertical chimneys over 75 and 125 in the scatter diagram, there is less vertical spread—therefore, less uncertainty in the predictions—in the chimney over 75.

11. $r = -1$: number wrong $= 10 -$ number right, so all the points on a scatter diagram (for number wrong vs. number right) lie on a straight line which slopes down. Also see exercise 9 on p. 106.

12. (a) Three students got 91 on the first count and 82 on the second, so they probably worked together. Another three got 85 on both counts; however, since that is the right answer, these students are probably just good counters.

    (b) False.

Chapter 9. More About Correlation

1. When studying one variable, you can use a graph called a <u>histogram</u>. When studying the relationship between two variables, you can use a graph called a <u>scatter diagram</u>.

2. (a) False. The scatter diagram slopes down: if x is below average, y is generally above average.

   (b) False. For example, height at age 9 is usually less than height at age 18, but the correlation is positive.

3. (a) Height at 16 and 18. It is easier to predict 2 years ahead than 14.

    (b) Height. Environment, personality, etc. affect weight more than height, and introduce more variability around the line.

    (c) Age 4: by age 18, these other factors have had more time to introduce variability.

4. Somewhat higher; see exercise set B, pp. 145ff.

5. (a) 7: the line $y = 2x - 1$ goes through $(1, 1)$ and $(2, 3)$, then through $(4, 7)$.

    (b) Not possible: $(1, 1)$, $(2, 3)$, and $(3, 4)$ do not lie on a line.

6. No. Data set (ii) is obtained by adding 3 to the y-values in data set (i), so r has to be the same for both. See p. 141.

7. No: section 4.

8. False. The data are cross-sectional, not longitudinal. Younger people were born later and educational levels have been going up over time.

9. (a) False: $r \approx -0.57$. The two sections (C and I) that liked their TA best did worst.

    (b) True: there is no pattern in the scatter diagram ($r \approx 0.12$).

    (c) False: there is a moderate, positive association ($r \approx 0.46$).

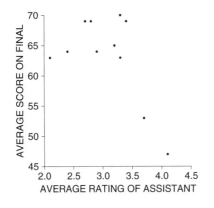
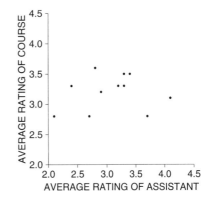

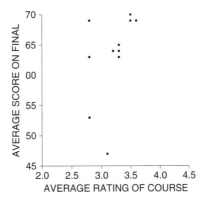

10. (a) True. The test-takers are a self-selected group, and good students are more
        likely to take the test. Hence, if a larger percentage of high school graduates
        take the test, the average skill level goes down.

     (b) False. The average in Connecticut is lower—but the reason may be that in
        Connecticut, a higher percentage of students take the test.

     Comment. See note 14 to chapter 9.

11. Quite a bit less. See section 4, and exercise set B on pp. 145ff.

12. (a) Education is measured in whole years (years of schooling completed).

     (b) Some dots correspond to many couples. For example, in many families, the
        husband and the wife both have 12 years of education (high school degree).
        All such families are plotted on the (12, 12) dot.

     (c) A (iv)   B (iii)   C (i)

Chapter 10. Regression

1. A (i)   B (iii)   C (ii)

2. (a) 112. Work: 115 is 1 SD above average at age 18, so the estimate at age 35
        is above average by r SDs. This is $0.8 \times 15 = 12$ points.

     (b) 112. See section 3.

3. (a) 64 inches   (b) 62 inches   (c) 63 inches, the average   (d) same as (c)

     Work for (a). The husband is 4 inches, or $4/2.7 \approx 1.5$ SDs above average in
     height. The wife is predicted to be above average in height by

     $$r \times 1.5 = 0.25 \times 1.5 \approx 0.4 \text{ SDs.}$$

     This is $0.4 \times 2.5 = 1$ inch.

4. (a) 15 years.

     (b) 13.5 years.

     (c) Appearances are deceiving; all that is going on here is the regression effect
        (section 5).

5. (a) False (unless there is something special about the SDs and the point of
        averages).

     (b) False: r measures association not causation.

     (c) True.

     (d) True: the correlation between y and x equals the correlation between x
        and y.

     (e) False: r measures association not causation.

6. Dashed: y on x.

     Dotted: SD line.

     Solid: x on y.

     See section 5.

7. So far, it looks like the regression effect (section 4).

8. The regression effect can't explain a change in the average for the whole population. The data suggest that patients are more relaxed the second time.

9. (a) 21% (b) 65% (c) 50% (d) 50%

   Work for (a). This student was 1.65 SDs below average on the midterm—

   He should be $r \times 1.65 = 0.5 \times 1.65 \approx 0.8$ SDs below average on the final. Now for the percentile rank on the final—

10. False. This person is likely to be between the 40th and 50th percentiles— regression effect (sections 3–4).

Chapter 11. The R.M.S. Error for Regression

1. Option (v): see p. 186.

2. Something is wrong. GPAs run from 0 to 4. If you predict 2, the maximum error is 2. The computer should be doing better than that.

3. (a) $\sqrt{1 - 0.8^2} \times 2.5 = 1.5$ inches.
   (b) $\sqrt{1 - 0.8^2} \times 1.7 \approx 1.0$ inches.

4. (a) r.m.s. error $= \sqrt{1 - r^2} \times$ SD of final scores $= 12$.
   (b) 65.8. This student is $30/25 = 1.2$ SDs above average on the midterm, and should be above average on the final by $r \times 1.2 = 0.72$ SDs. That is 10.8 points.
   (c) 12, the r.m.s. error: see part (a). It is OK to use the r.m.s. error inside a strip because the diagram is football-shaped.

5. (a) The answer is about 5%.

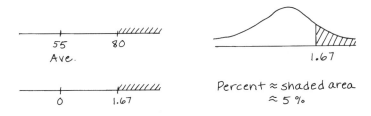

(b) New average ≈ 65.8, new SD = 12, (80 − 65.8)/12 ≈ 1.18; the answer is about 12%.

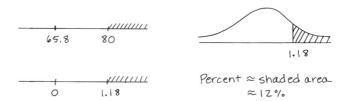

6. No. The conclusion seems right, but does not follow from the data. It could be, for example, that better students spend more time doing homework anyway.

7. Option (iii) is right: regression effect.

8. (a) The procedure is subject to error; replication gives more accuracy.

    (b) Two examples of replication: (i) basing course grades on a midterm and final, not just the final; (ii) getting a second opinion before surgery.

9. This is probably the regression effect.

10. If the regression method was used, and you plot the "2006 predicted" against the "2005 actual," you have to get a line—the regression line. Here, the plot is not linear. The regression method was not used to predict 2006 from 2005. (The "actual 2006" column is not needed for the solution.)

11. There are a lot of people with 9, 13, and 17 years of education; very few with 8, 12 or 16: and nobody with 0, although three people have 1 year of education. It looks as if 1 year got added to educational levels, by mistake.

    Comment. The Current Population Survey has public use data sets, which have a fairly complicated file structure. A programmer made an error reading the file, and we caught it by looking at this kind of picture.

12. True, although the difference is pretty small. The correlation is negative: the men with 20 years of eduction should have blood pressures which are, on average, below the grand average by about 3 mm (by the regression method). In other words, the men with 20 years of education should have average blood pressures of about 116 mm.

Chapter 12. The Regression Line

1. In a run of 1 SD, the regression line rises $r \times$ SD. The slope is $0.60 \times 20/10 = 1.2$ final points per midterm point. The intercept is $55 - 1.2 \times 70 = -29$. So the equation is

    predicted final score = $1.2 \times$ midterm score $- 29$.

2. Predicted income is ($1600 per inch) × height − $81,400. Taller people make more money, on average. Probably, this reflects other variables in family background; although looking every inch an executive may not hurt.

3. Obviously not. The slope means that the 151-pound men are taller, on average, than the 150-pound men—by around 0.0267 inches. Similarly, the men who weigh 152 pounds are on average a little taller than the men who weigh 151 pounds. And so forth.

4. (a) The r.m.s. error is about 1. The points are 1 or so above or below the line.

   (b) No. The scatter diagram slopes down, and so would the regression line; this line is horizontal.

5. This is not legitimate. There are two regression lines. The one for predicting husbands from wives has slope 0.375. See section 10.5.

6. The slope stays the same, and the intercept goes up by 10%.

7. The slope has to be 0.5, because the regression line has to go through the point of averages.

8. (a) True. (b) False. (c) False. (d) True. (e) True.
   Comment. See section 12.2.

9. This is the regression line of IQ on parental income—in disguise (section 10.2). The slope is

   $r \times$ SD of IQ/SD of income $= 0.50 \times 15/45{,}000 = 1/6000$.

10. $150,000 is likely to be too high. You need the other regression line, for income on IQ (section 10.5). A better estimate is $105,000.

11. Something is wrong with the equation. The regression line has to go through the point of averages. This line doesn't.

12. No. There doesn't even seem to be any consistent direction to the association.

Part IV. Probability

Chapter 13. What Are The Chances?

1. (a) False. Chances have to be between 0% (can't happen) and 100% (must happen). See p. 223.

   (b) True. The event will happen about 9 times out of 10, and the opposite event will happen the remaining 1 time out of 10. See p. 223.

2. Option (i) is better: you only have to jump one hurdle rather than two.

3. Option (ii) is better, because there are a lot more ways to win:

   clubs diamonds hearts spades
   hearts diamonds clubs spades
   etc.

4. $4/52 \times 3/51 \times 2/50 \times 1/49 \times 4/48 \approx 1/3{,}000{,}000$.

5. Yes. If the ticket is white, then there are two chances in three to get the number 1, and one chance in three to get 8. And the same for black.

6. (a) True.

    (b) True. See example 2 on p. 226.

    (c) False. The two events are dependent. See example 4 on p. 229. The chance
        is $1/52 \times 1/51$, not $1/52 \times 1/52$.

7. (a) False. (b) False. (c) True.

    Both sequences are equally likely, having chance $1/2^6$. Of course, there are a
    lot more sequences with 3 heads and 3 tails, but that's not the question.

8. (a) On one roll, the chance of getting 3 or more spots is $4/6 \approx 0.67$; the chance
        of getting 3 or more spots on 4 rolls is $(0.67)^4 \approx 0.20$, or 20%.

    (b) None of the rolls show 3 or more spots if all show 2 or fewer, and the chance
        is $(2/6)^4 \approx 0.012$, or 1.2%

    (c) $100\% - 20\% = 80\%$.

    Comment. Compare the two propositions,

            (i) "not all the rolls show 3 or more spots," and

            (ii) "none of the rolls show 3 or more spots."

    Proposition (i) is easier, and has a bigger chance. For example, suppose the
    dice land 4 6 5 2. Then (i) holds—the last roll was less than 3. But (ii) does
    not—the first roll is bigger than 3. (So were the second and third rolls.)

9. (a) $(1/6)^{10} = 1/60,466,176$.

    (b) $1 - 1/60,466,176 \approx 1$.

    (c) $(5/6)^{10} \approx 0.16$, or 16%.

    Comment. Not getting 10 sixes is easier than getting 10 non-sixes.

10. Option (ii) is better. You have the same 50–50 chance of winning $1, but you
    can't lose.

11. Yes. The tickets are 1 1, 1 2, 1 2, 1 3, 3 1, 3 2, 3 2, 3 3.

12. $3/100 \times 2/99 \times 1/98 \approx 6/1,000,000$.

Chapter 14. More About Chance

1. (a) The chance is $1/6 \times 1/6 = 1/36$.

    (b) The chance is $6/36 = 1/6$; see figure 1 in chapter 14. Or use part (a) and
        the addition rule. Here is yet another argument. Imagine one of the dice is
        white and the other is black: no matter how the white one lands, the black
        one has 1 chance in 6 to match it.

2. From figure 1 in chapter 14, the chance is 2/36.

3. (a) False. These events aren't mutually exclusive, so you can't add the chances. (To find the chance, read section 14.4.)

   (b) False. Same reason.

4. Option (i) is better. Even if you miss the first time, you get a second try at the money.

5. (a) False. A and B can happen together, with chance $1/3 \times 1/10$. So they aren't mutually exclusive.

   (b) True. If A happens, the chance of B drops to 0. That's an extreme form of dependence.

6. If you want to find the chance that <u>at least one of the two events</u> will happen, check to see if they are <u>mutually exclusive</u>; if so, you can <u>add</u> the chances.

   If you want to find the chance that <u>both events</u> will happen, check to see if they are <u>independent</u>; if so, you can <u>multiply</u> the chances.

7. This is like Chevalier de Méré: the chance is $1 - (3/5)^4 \approx 87\%$.

8. 100%—you can't avoid it.

9. Draw a picture like figure 1—

1 1	1 2	1 3	1 4
2 1	2 2	2 3	2 4
3 1	3 2	3 3	3 4

   For instance, 3 2 means you got 3 from box A and 2 from box B. There are 12 outcomes, and each has chance 1/12.

   (a) The good outcomes are 2 1, 3 1, 3 2; the chance is $3/12 = 25\%$.

   (b) $3/12 = 25\%$.

   (c) $100\% - (25\% + 25\%) = 50\%$.

10. Option (ii) is better. There are 60 rolls, and 60 draws. On each roll you have 2 chances in 6 to win \$1 and 4 chances in 6 to get nothing; but on each draw, you have 3 chances in 6 to win \$1 and 3 chances in 6 to win nothing.

11. (a) $13/52 \times 12/51 \times 11/50 \approx 1\%$.

    (b) $39/52 \times 38/51 \times 37/50 \approx 41\%$.

    (c) The chance of getting all diamonds is 1%, see (a). The chance of not getting all diamonds is 99%.

    Comment. "No diamonds" and "not all diamonds" are two different propositions.

12. Both statements are true. Getting ten heads in a row is very unlikely—before you start tossing. If you get nine heads in a row, however, the chance is 50–50 to get a tenth head. (It is the multiplication of all those 50–50 chances that makes ten heads in a row so unlikely.)

13. By trial and error, $(0.98)^{34} \approx 0.503$, and $(0.98)^{35} \approx 0.493$. With 34 draws, there is a 49.7% chance of getting a red marble; with 35 draws, the chance is 50.7%. The answer is 35. (Logs are a more sophisticated option.)

14. The chances are the same. Each ticket has the same (tiny) chance of winning. If you win the grand prize with one ticket, you can't win the grand prize with the other. So, buying two different tickets doubles your chance—addition rule.

Chapter 15. The Binomial Formula

1. The chance is

$$\frac{6!}{1!5!} \left(\frac{1}{6}\right)^1 \left(\frac{5}{6}\right)^5 \approx 40\%.$$

2. The chance of not getting a six in one roll is 5/6, and option (iii) does it by the multiplication rule. (Or use the binomial formula.)

3. The chance of getting 4 girls is $(1/2)^4 = 1/16$. The chance of getting 3 girls is 4/16, by the binomial formula. The total chance is 5/16, by the addition rule.

4. False. The binomial formula does not apply. The draws are dependent, because they are made without replacement.

5. True. The first person gets $8!/(2!6!) = 28$ committees. (Write the 8 names out in a row; then put down 2 C's and 6 N's under the names, where C means "in the committee" and N means "not in the committee"; the binomial coefficient tells you how many ways there are to do that.)

   By similar reasoning, the second person gets $8!/(5!3!) = 56$ committees.

6. False: $8!/(2!6!) = 8!/(6!2!)$.

7. Yes. There are 10 ways to draw two R's and three G's. Each way has the same chance. The total chance is the sum of these 10 chances, that is, 10 times the common value $(1/10)^2(9/10)^3$. The addition rule applies because the ways are mutually exclusive: for example, if you get R R G G G, you cannot get G G G R R.

8. The chance of getting 2 heads among the first 5 tosses is

$$\frac{5!}{2!3!} \left(\frac{1}{2}\right)^5.$$

The chance of getting 4 heads among the last 5 tosses is

$$\frac{5!}{4!1!} \left(\frac{1}{2}\right)^5.$$

The first 5 tosses are independent of the last 5. So the answer is

$$\frac{5!}{2!3!} \left(\frac{1}{2}\right)^5 \times \frac{5!}{4!1!} \left(\frac{1}{2}\right)^5 = \frac{50}{1024} \approx 5\%.$$

9. (a) (i): multiplication rule.

    (b) (viii): the chance is 0.

    (c) (iv): addition rule.

    (d) (viii): the events are not mutually exclusive.

    Comment: the chance is $2/52 - 1/52 \times 1/51$

    (e) (vii)

10. Without—then it's bound to happen.

11. The probabilities are 0.8 of 1% for all-cause mortality, 0.2 of 1% for coronary heart disease, and 25% for lung cancer.

    For part (d), the difference in death rates would be very hard to explain by genetics: these twins are genetically identical. For all-cause mortality or heart disease, the difference would be hard to explain by chance. For lung cancer, the difference can be explained by chance. In all cases, the difference can be explained by the health effects of smoking.

    The arithmetic for (a):

    $$\binom{22}{17} = 26{,}334 \qquad \binom{22}{20} = 231$$

    $$\binom{22}{18} = 7{,}315 \qquad \binom{22}{21} = 22$$

    $$\binom{22}{19} = 1{,}540 \qquad \binom{22}{22} = 1$$

    Next, $2^{22} = 4{,}194{,}304$. So the chance is

    $$\frac{26{,}334 + 7{,}315 + 1{,}540 + 231 + 22 + 1}{4{,}194{,}304} \approx 0.8 \text{ of } 1\%.$$

    Comments. The constitutional hypothesis is not tenable for all-cause mortality or death from coronary heart disease. On lung cancer, these data do not refute Fisher. Confounding (e.g., by socio-economic status) is a possibility, but not likely: twins are very similar in many respects.

Chapter 15. Special Review Exercise

1. False. The population got bigger too. You need to look at the number of murders relative to total population size. The population in 1990 was about 249 million, and in 1970 it was about 203 million: 20,273 out of 249 million is actually a bit less than 16,848 out of 203 million.

    Comment. The murder rate declined sharply from 1990 to 2000.

2. (a) No. The comparison was with patients treated by other methods in the past.

(b) No. Ullyot was using historical controls, which is not such a good idea—such studies are often biased in favor of treatment. See section 1.3. (Randomized controlled trials were much less positive about the value of coronary bypass surgery.)

3. False. The selection ratio for the pooled data is 68.5%. This is like Simpson's Paradox (pp. 17ff). A majority of the women took the test in 1977, when the pass rates were higher.

Technical comment. In the pooled data, the women's pass rate is a weighted average of their pass rates for 1975 and 1977, and must be intermediate between those two values. Likewise for the men. The selection ratio, however, is a more complicated statistic. The selection ratio in the pooled data can be written as

$$\frac{79 \times \frac{10}{79} + 102 \times \frac{18}{102}}{79 + 102} \Bigg/ \frac{1312 \times \frac{250}{1312} + 1259 \times \frac{331}{1259}}{1312 + 1259}$$

which equals

$$\frac{79 \times 0.1266 + 102 \times 0.1765}{79 + 102} \Bigg/ \frac{1312 \times 0.1905 + 1259 \times 0.2629}{1312 + 1259}.$$

The women are in the numerator; the men, in the denominator. The weights for the women and for the men differ. The women get more weight on the higher pass rate (102 on 0.1765 vs 79 on 0.1266), while the men get more weight on the lower pass rate (1312 on 0.1905 vs 1259 on 0.2629). If the weights are not constrained, the lower bound on the selection ratio in the pooled data is $0.1266/0.2629 \approx 48.16\%$, the numerator being the smaller of the women's two pass rates and the denominator being the larger of the men's two rates. Likewise, the upper bound is $0.1765/0.1905 \approx 92.65\%$. The observed selection ratio of 68.5% is well inside the permissible range.

4. Only (a) is right; (b) has area about 200%, and (c) has the wrong units.

5. About 1 year. One month is way too small (for instance, 68% of the students can hardly be within one month of average); 5 years is too large.

6. False. These data are cross sectional, not longitudinal. The 50-year-old men were born in 1955, and went to school when educational levels were lower than they are now. Furthermore, the material taught was less relevant to today's economy. In these respects, the 60-year-olds are in worse shape. Education is one reason why the curve of age-specific average incomes flattens out. The effect of education is confounded with the effect of age.

Comment. Other data suggests that for each birth cohort, average income increases fairly steadily with age.

7. False. From left to right, the areas of the blocks are 10%, 10%, 10%, 30%, 40%. The 30th percentile is 60, and the 60th percentile is 80. Generally, the 60th percentile will not be twice the 30th percentile. (Remember, a percentile is a number on the horizontal axis of the histogram.)

8. (a) True. List (ii) is obtained by doubling each entry on list (i), then adding 1. This change of scale cancels on conversion to standard units (section 5.6).

   (b) False. List (ii) is obtained by doubling each entry on list (i), changing the sign, then adding 1. This changes the signs in standard units.

9. (a) The 70th percentile is about 0.52 in standard units, or 60 in original units. The 80th percentile is about 0.84 in standard units, or 67 in original units. The brothers are separated by about 7 points.

   (b) The sisters are separated by about 9 points.

   Comment. As you go further into the tails of the normal distribution, each extra percentile covers a greater and greater distance in the original units—because the normal curve gets lower and lower.

10. It's fine. (The data are from the March 2005 Current Population Survey.)

11. (a) $r \approx 0.82$.

    (b) Can't be done, the points $(8, 9)$ and $(8, 13)$ cannot fall on the same line. (If all the points fall on a vertical line, the correlation is undefined—not the case here.)

12. (a) True.

    (b) True. The correlation between y and x equals the correlation between x and y.

    (c) False, as (a) and (b) should demonstrate.

    (d) False.

13. (i) Nearly 0. (ii) Nearly 1. (iii) Nearly -1.

14. Solid: (i)

    Dotted: (iii)

    Dashed: (ii)

15. The r.m.s. error of the regression line is $\sqrt{1 - 0.55^2} \times 12 \approx 10$. About 68% of the data is within ± 10 points of the regression line, and 16% is above the line by 10 points or more. (The other 16% is below the line by 10 points or more.) The answer is 16%.

16. Statistics—regression effect.

17. The 25th percentile on the final is about 0.675 in standard units, about 73.5 in original units. In other words, of the students who scored around 50 on the midterm, you need to find the percentage scoring over 73.5 on the final. The new average is 60, the new SD is 16, and 73.5 is 0.84 in standard units. The answer is given by the area under the normal curve to the right of 0.84, which is about 20%.

18. There are 30 possible outcomes, all equally likely, shown in the table below.

$$
\begin{array}{cccccc}
1\ 1 & 1\ 2 & 1\ 3 & 1\ 4 & 1\ 5 & 1\ 6 \\
2\ 1 & 2\ 2 & 2\ 3 & 2\ 4 & 2\ 5 & 2\ 6 \\
3\ 1 & 3\ 2 & 3\ 3 & 3\ 4 & 3\ 5 & 3\ 6 \\
4\ 1 & 4\ 2 & 4\ 3 & 4\ 4 & 4\ 5 & 4\ 6 \\
5\ 1 & 5\ 2 & 5\ 3 & 5\ 4 & 5\ 5 & 5\ 6 \\
\end{array}
$$

For instance, 3 2 means you got 3 from box A and 2 from box B.

(a) There are two good outcomes (2 5 and 5 2), the chance is 2/30.

(b) 5/30.

(c) 10/30. You have to look at the table, and count. The good outcomes are shown below, the bad ones are replaced by "x x."

$$
\begin{array}{cccccc}
\text{x x} & \text{x x} & 1\ 3 & 1\ 4 & 1\ 5 & 1\ 6 \\
\text{x x} & \text{x x} & \text{x x} & \text{x x} & 2\ 5 & 2\ 6 \\
3\ 1 & \text{x x} & \text{x x} & \text{x x} & \text{x x} & \text{x x} \\
4\ 1 & \text{x x} & \text{x x} & \text{x x} & \text{x x} & \text{x x} \\
5\ 1 & 5\ 2 & \text{x x} & \text{x x} & \text{x x} & \text{x x} \\
\end{array}
$$

19. (a) You have to get 3 non-hearts (clubs, diamonds, spades), then a heart. The chance is $39/52 \times 38/51 \times 37/50 \times 13/49 \approx 11\%$.

(b) $13/49 \approx 27\%$. Here, you are asked to compute a conditional chance—of getting a heart on the 4th card, given the first 3 cards were not hearts.

20. If you get 7 heads, you automatically get 3 tails. Use the binomial formula (chapter 15):

$$
\frac{10!}{7!3!} \left(\frac{1}{2}\right)^{10} = \frac{120}{1024} \approx 12\%.
$$

PART V. Chance Variability

Chapter 16. The Law of Averages

1. Option (iii) is the best. The chance error is not likely to be 0 exactly, but should be small relative to the number of draws.

2. Now option (i) is it.

3. Both are wrong. Luck and the law of averages have nothing to do with it—the chances stay the same, every time.

4. (a) 60 rolls. With more rolls, the percentage of aces will be closer to $16\frac{2}{3}\%$. You want the percentage of aces to be far from $16\frac{2}{3}\%$. Chance error in the percentages is working against you, choose the smaller number of rolls.

(b) 600 rolls. Now chance error in the percentages is working for you, choose the larger number of rolls.

    (c) 600 rolls. Like (b).

    (d) 60 rolls. As you roll more and more, there get to be more and more pos-
sibilities, no particular one can be very likely. Take a more extreme case:
with 6000 rolls, you can get 1000 aces, or 1001, or 1002, ... There are
lots of possibilities, each one individually has a small chance.

5.   False. If the number of heads is 50, the percentage of heads is 50%. (It is not
so likely that the number of heads will be 50 exactly, section 1.)

6.   Possibility (i) is better. Reason: $10/15 = 20/30 = 2/3$. Option (i) is like tossing
a coin 15 times, and asking for 2/3 or more heads. Option (ii) ups the number
of tosses to 30. With the bigger number of tosses, you are less likely to get 2/3
or more heads. This is like exercise 4(a).

7.   The score is like the sum of 25 draws from the box $\boxed{4 \ {-}1 \ {-}1 \ {-}1 \ {-}1}$.

8.   The net gain is like the sum of 50 draws from a box with 4 tickets marked "$8"
and 34 tickets marked "−$1."

9.   Choose (ii). With more draws, the percentage of reds is likely to be closer to
the percentage in the box, therefore, above 50%. (When the percentage of reds
among the draws is above 50%, more reds are drawn than blues, and you win
the dollar.) Exercise 9 is like exercise 4(b) or 6.

10. (a) $30/200 = 0.15$.   (b) −0.1.   (c) Average = sum/200.

    (d) The same: $5/200 = 0.025$, so the options describe the same event in
different language.

Chapter 17. The Expected Value and Standard Error

1.   (a) 100, 1000.

    (b) The average of the box is 7 and the SD is 3. So the expected value for the
sum is $100 \times 7 = 700$ and the SE is $\sqrt{100} \times 3 = 30$. The sum will be
around 700, give or take 30 or so. The chance is about 90%.

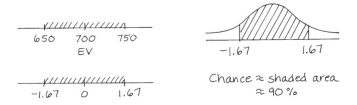

2.   (a) The net gain is like the sum of 100 draws made at random with replacement
from a box with 12 tickets marked "$2" and 26 tickets marked "−$1." The
average of the box is $-\$2/38 \approx -\$0.05$, and the SD is

$$[\$2 - (-\$1)] \times \sqrt{\frac{12}{38} \times \frac{26}{38}} \approx \$1.39$$

The net gain will be around $100 \times (-\$0.05) = -\$5$, give or take

$$\sqrt{100} \times \$1.39 = \$14 \text{ or so.}$$

(b) The number of wins is like the sum of 100 draws made from a box with 12 tickets marked "1" and 26 marked "0." The number will be around 32, give or take 5 or so.

(c) Both bets pay 2 to 1, but roulette gives you a better chance of winning— $12/38 \approx 32\%$ compared to 25% for Keno. You lose faster at Keno.

3. (a) (iii), see section 4. (b) (i) (c) (v) (d) (iv) (e) (ii)

4. The number of aces in 180 rolls of a die is like the sum of 180 draws from a box with 1 ticket marked "1" and 5 tickets marked "0." The number of aces will be around 30, give or take 5 or so. There is about a 99.7% chance that the number of aces will be in the range 15 to 45. About 99.7% of the people should get a number in that range.

5. The larger number is worse; the chance error is likely to be larger (in absolute terms) with the larger number of throws.

6.

12	chance error in the sum of the draws
45	observed value for the number of 1's
187	observed value for the sum of the draws
25	expected value for the number of 3's
50	expected value for the number of 1's
175	expected value for the sum of the draws
5	standard error for the number of 1's
32	observed value for the number of 3's

7. (a) $321/100 = 3.21$. (b) $3.78 \times 100 = 378$.

   (c) The average of the draws will be between 3 and 4 when the sum is between 300 and 400. The expected value for the sum is 350, and the SE is

   $$\sqrt{100} \times 1.7 = 17,$$

   so the chance is about 99.7%.

8. (a) Option (ii) is right. The sum is equally likely to go up or down 1 on each draw, just like the difference. Option (i) is out, you can't add words. With option (iii), the sum can't go up. With option (iv), the sum can't go down. With option (v), the sum has a chance to stand still, but the difference has to go up or down.

   (b) Expected value $= 0$, SE $= \sqrt{100} = 10$.

9. (a) is false, (b) and (c) are true. The reason: if you play (i), the net gain is like the sum of 1000 draws from a box with 12 tickets marked $2 and 26 marked $-$1.

The average of the the box is −$2/38 and the SD is about $1.39. The expected value for the net gain is −$53 and the SE is $44. If you play (ii), there is another box, with a bigger SD. The net gain has the same expected value but the SE is $182. Chance variability helps you overcome the negative expected value, so you are more likely to come out ahead with B. Chance variability also makes it more likely that you will lose big.

The chance of coming out ahead with (i) is about 12%.

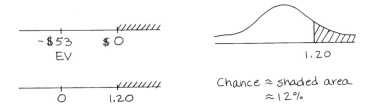

The chance of coming out ahead with (ii) is about 38%.

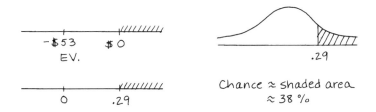

10. Statement (iii) is false. The SE goes not go up by the full factor of 2, but only $\sqrt{2} \approx 1.4$. Unless there is something rather strange about the box, the chance that the sum is between 700 and 900 will be quite a bit more than 75%.

11. You have to change the box, to $\boxed{0\ 0\ 0\ 1\ 3}$. The average of the box is 0.8, and the SD is about 1.2. So the sum will be around 80, give or take 12 or so.

12. In all three cases, the expected value is 400 and the SE is 20: the expected value and SE are computed from the box, not the draws. The chance errors are 31, −14, and 17. Remember, Sum = Expected Value + Chance Error.

13. The number of A's is like the sum of 1000 draws made at random with replacement from $\boxed{1\ 0\ 1\ 0\ 0\ 1}$. The SD of the box is 0.50. By the square root law, the SE for number of A's is $\sqrt{1000} \times 0.50$. The number of B's is like the sum of draws made at random with replacement from $\boxed{0\ 0\ 0\ 1\ 0\ 0}$. The SD of the box is $\sqrt{1/6 \times 5/6} \approx 0.37$, so the SE for the number of B's is $\sqrt{1000} \times 0.37$. The SE for the number of A's is larger than for B's. The number of A's is more likely to be 10 or more above expected, because the SE is larger.

Comment for mathematicians. More generally, let N be the number of draws:

a careful asymptotic argument would separate the cases $N = 6n + r$ for $r = 0, 1, 2, 3, 4, 5$. A delicate case is $r = 2$.

14. The house has 36 chances out of 38 to break even, and 2 chances in 38 to win $2. In round numbers, the house makes money 5 times, give or take 2 or so. It wins about $10, give or take $4 or so.

Comment. Part (b) follows from (a).

Chapter 18. The Normal Approximation for Probability Histograms

1. 20, 25.

2. (a) The average of the box is 4 and the SD is about 2.24. The EV for the sum is 1600 and the SE is about $\sqrt{400} \times 2.24 \approx 45$. The chance is about 99%.

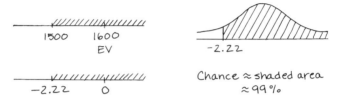

(b) The number of 3's is like the sum of 400 draws from the box $\boxed{0\ 1\ 0\ 0}$. The expected number is 100 and the SE is 8.66. The chance is about 12%.

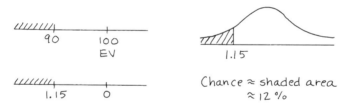

Comment. For more accuracy, use the continuity correction on part (b),

3. The chance that the sum will be in the interval from 10 to 20 inclusive equals the area under the probability histogram between 9.5 and 20.5. The normal curve is the approximation, the histogram is the truth. You start at 9.5 on the left to catch the block over 10, representing the chance that the sum will be 10. Likewise, you stop at 20.5 on the right to catch the block over 20.

4. If you get 12 heads, you automatically get 13 tails. The chance of getting 12 heads can be found using the method of chapter 15:

$$\binom{25}{12} \times \left(\frac{1}{2}\right)^{25} = \frac{5,200,300}{33,554,432} \approx 15.50\%$$

Or, use the method of example 1 on p. 317. The expected number of heads is 12.5, and the SE is 2.5. The normal curve gives a very good approximation:

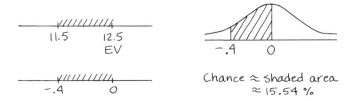

5. (i) is the probability histogram for the sum, it's like the normal curve.
   (ii) is the probability histogram for the product, it's like figure 10, p. 323.
   (iii) is the histogram for the numbers drawn, it's like a histogram for the numbers in the box.

6. Something is wrong with COIN. With a million tosses, the number of heads should be around 500,000 give or take 500 or so. COIN is 4 SEs too high. (The SE for the number of heads is a tiny fraction of the number of tosses.)

7. Option (ii) is right. With (i), all the values have equal chances, and that's wrong (figure 1, p. 311, bottom panel.)

8. (a) is true, (b) is false, (c) is false, (d) is true.
   The expected value is computed without error, as 50. The 5 represents the likely size of the chance error in the number of heads, not in the expected value.

9. (a) is true, (b) is false, you don't have enough draws to use the normal approximation. See exercise 6, p. 324.

   Technical comment. If you use the continuity correction, the normal approximation is not ridiculous—for this symmetric interval.

10. Both statements are true. With more tosses, the probability histogram gets closer to the normal curve. You get a feeling for how many draws are enough by looking at the pictures in the chapter.

11. The sum of the draws is 270, with EV = 250 and SE = 15; the chance error is 20, which is 1.33 SEs. The number of 1's is 17, with EV = 25 and SE $\approx$ 4.33; the chance error is -8, which is about -1.8 SEs. The number of 2's is 54, with EV = 50 and SE = 5; the chance error is 4, which is 0.8 SEs.
    (a) number of 2's   (b) sum of the draws

12. (a) Can't be done. For example, the box could have 4 tickets marked "1" and 6 marked "-10," or 4 marked "3" and 6 marked "-2." With these two boxes, the chances would be quite different.

    (b) Can be done, using the normal approximation—that's why the average and SD are so useful.

13. Can't be done. You need to know how many 3's there are in the box.

14. This is like drawing at random with replacement from a box with 4 tickets marked "1" and 6 marked "0," and asking for the chance that the sum of the

draws will be 425 or more. The normal approximation will be fine. (The average and SD of the original numbers in the box are irrelevant.)

15. Very fishy. Very. The chance of getting a red marble is 40%, so the expected number of reds is 40; the chance of getting 39 or fewer is about 50% (or a little less). All 10 counts are below 40—an event of probability $1/2^{10}$.

Part VI. Sampling

Chapter 19. Sample Surveys

1. False. Simple random samples are impractical for this purpose (section 4).

2. No, because of response bias. The subjects could try to give the interviewers the pleasing answer, rather than the true answer. (In this study, many respondents said they were using the product when they really weren't.)

3. No. This county might be exceptional. (It was.)

4. The people with college degrees were living in more suburban neighborhoods. This was not a good way to draw a sample.

5. This estimate is likely to be too high. With smaller households, the interviewer is less likely to find someone at home. So the survey procedure is, on average, replacing smaller households by larger ones.

6. No. Different sorts of students are more likely or less likely to walk through different parts of the campus at different times, and the chances are difficult or impossible to figure (p. 341).

7. Option (ii) is better. You win if number of heads is between 480 and 520. That's a broader range than (i).

8. Cannot be determined from the information given. The rectangle over a number might represent chance, or it might represent an empirical frequency. You need to know how the histogram was computed.

9. The smaller one. As the size of the hospital goes up, the percentage of male births gets closer to 52%, and is less likely to exceed 55%. See section 16.1.

10. Look at figure 3, chapter 18. The likeliest number of heads is 50: pick that first. Your next two picks should be 49 and 51. Then 48 and 52. And so forth. You should pick 45 through 55. And your chance of winning is about 73%—example 1(b) on p. 317.

11. (a) 10 through 20.   (b) 40 through 50.

    (c) To get the center of the range, take 50 from the sum; and then go 5 either way.

    (d) 73%, as in the previous exercise.

12. (a) Only the "high achievers" are listed in the sampling frame.

    (b) There seems to be quite a lot of room for bias here. How were the 5,000 students selected? What about non-response bias?

Chapter 20. Chance Errors in Sampling

1.

	No. of heads		Pct. of heads	
Number of tosses	Expected value	SE	Expected value	SE
100	50	5	50%	5%
2,500	1,250	25	50%	1%
10,000	5,000	50	50%	0.5 of 1%
1,000,000	500,000	500	50%	0.05 of 1%

2. The first step is setting up the box model. The number of aces is like the sum of 1000 draws from the box $\boxed{0\ 0\ 0\ 0\ 0\ 1}$. The average of the box is 1/6 and the SD is $\sqrt{1/6 \times 5/6} \approx 0.373$. The EV is $1000 \times 1/6 \approx 166.7$. The SE is $\sqrt{1000} \times 0.373 \approx 11.8$. The number of aces will be around 167, give or take 12 or so. The SE for the percentage is 12 out of 1000, which is 1.2%. The percentage of aces should be around $16\frac{2}{3}\%$, give or take 1.2% or so.

3. (a) There should be 50,000 tickets in the box. The box is the population—all 50,000 forms.

    (b) Each ticket shows a 0 (gross income under $50,000) or a 1 (gross income over $50,000).

    (c) False: the SD of the box is $\sqrt{0.2 \times 0.8} = 0.4$.

    (d) True. The draws are the sample.

    (e) The number of sample forms with gross incomes over $50,000 is like the sum of 900 draws from the box. The expected value for the sum is 180. The SE for the sum is $\sqrt{900} \times 0.4 = 12$. The number of sample forms with gross incomes over $50,000 will be around 180, give or take 12 or so. Now 12 out of 900 is about 1.33%. The percentage of forms in the sample with gross incomes over $50,000 will be 20.00%, give or take 1.33% or so. The chance is about 55%—

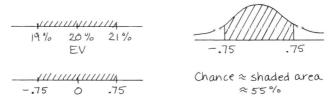

    (f) Can't be done with the information given. You need to know the percentage of forms with gross incomes over $75,000. And you can't use the normal curve, because these data are far from normal.

4. (a) 50,000. (b) A gross income. (c) True. (d) True.

The total gross income is like the sum of 900 draws from the box, whose average is $37,000. The SD is $20,000. The expected value for the total is $900 \times \$37,000 = \$33,300,000$. The SE is $\sqrt{900} \times \$20,000 = \$600,000$. The chance is about 69%.

MM = $ 1,000,000

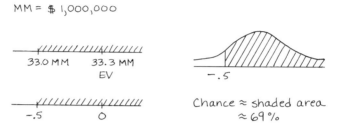

In exercise 3, you were classifying and counting, so you had to change the box; here, you are working with a sum, so it would be a bad idea to change the box.

5. The total weight of the group is like the sum of 50 draws from a box. The average of the box is 150 pounds and the SD is 35 pounds. The expected value for the sum is 7,500 pounds and the SE is $\sqrt{50} \times 35 \approx 250$ pounds. The chance is about 2%—maybe a better elevator is needed.

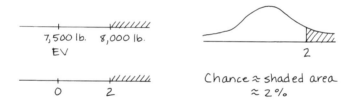

6. Option (ii) is right. In absolute terms, the California sample will be much bigger, and therefore more accurate for estimating percents; the size of the sample relative to the size of the state is basically irrelevant (section 4).

7. (a) is true and (b) is false. The expected value is computed with no chance error: the EV equals the percentage of 1's in the box.

(c) is true and (d) is false. The percentage of 1's among the draws will be off its expected value, due to chance error. The SE for the number of 1's among the draws is $\sqrt{500} \times \sqrt{0.25 \times 0.75} \approx 9.7$. The SE for the percentage of 1's among the draws is $(9.7/500) \times 100\% \approx 2\%$.

(e) is true and (f) is false: you know what's in the box.

8. The expected value for the percentage of democrats in the sample is 40%. The normal curve can be used to figure chances here (p. 364), because the sample is reasonably large. Half the area under the curve is to the right of 0, and 0 in standard units is just the expected value. In other words, there is just about

a 50% chance for the sample percentage to exceed the population percentage. So, 40% goes into the blank.

9. The number of 1's is the sum of the draws. The expected value is 200, and the SE is about 12.

10. It's fine. (This chapter is about the SE for percentages, but the idea of computing SEs for numbers should not disappear.)

11. (a) 357, 340.   (b) 71.4%, 68%.

    Comment. The expected value is computed from the box; the observed value, from the sample.

12. The total number of interviews is like the sum of 400 draws from a box. The average of the box is 2.38, and the SD is 1.87. The total number of interviews will be around $400 \times 2.38 = 952$, give or take $\sqrt{400} \times 1.87 \approx 37$ or so.

Chapter 21. The Accuracy of Percentages

1. The number in the sample who approve of the Mayor is like the sum of 1000 draws made at random without replacement from a box with a ticket for each registered voter in the town; the ticket is marked "1" if the voter approves of the Mayor and "0" otherwise.

2. (a) The sample is like 500 draws from a box with 25,000 tickets; each ticket is marked 1 (has a computer) or 0 (does not have a computer). The number of sample households with computers is like the sum of the draws.

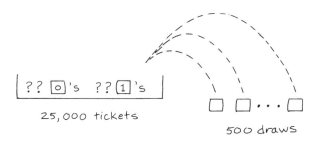

    The fraction of 1's in the box is unknown, but can be estimated by the fraction in the sample, as $239/500 = 0.478$. On this basis, the SD of the box is estimated as $\sqrt{0.478 \times 0.522} \approx 0.50$. The SE for the number of sample households with computers is estimated as $\sqrt{500} \times 0.50 \approx 11$, and 11 out of 500 is 2.2%. The percentage of households in the town with internet access is estimated as 47.8%, and the estimate is likely to be off by 2.2% or so.

    (b) The 95%-confidence interval is $47.8\% \pm 4.4\%$.

    Comment. You need to estimate the percentage for the town from data for the town: the national figures may not apply. (In this case, the town seems pretty close to the national average.)

3. (a) 1.4%, 0.5 of 1%.

(b) Hard to do: the box is lopsided and the normal approximation won't work very well. (See exercises 5–6 on p. 324; exercises 3–4 on p. 383.)

4. In the sample, $(172 + 207)/500 = 379/500 = 75.8\%$ of the households owned cars. The percentage of households in the town with cars is estimated as 75.8%, give or take 1.9% or so.

5. (a) The box has millions of tickets, one for each 17-year-old in school that year. Tickets are marked 1 for those who knew that Chaucer wrote *The Canterbury Tales*, and 0 for the others. The data are like 6000 draws from the box, and the number of students in the sample who know the answer is like the sum of the draws. The fraction of 1's in the box can be estimated from the sample as 0.361. On this basis, the SD of the box is estimated as $\sqrt{0.361 \times 0.639} \approx 0.48$. The SE for the number of students in the sample who know the answer is estimated as $\sqrt{6000} \times 0.48 \approx 37$. The SE for the percentage is 37/6000, which is about 0.6 of 1%. The percentage of students in the population who know the answer is estimated as 36.1%, give or take 0.6 of 1% or so. The 95%-confidence interval is $36.1\% \pm 1.2\%$.

(b) $95.2\% \pm 0.6$ of 1%.

6. False, because of chance error. The sample percentage is likely to be close to the population percentage, but not exactly equal. The SE for the percentage says how far off you can expect to be.

7. This is not the right SE. We do not have a simple random sample of 252 days, and the daily changes are dependent: each day's closing price is the next day's opening price.

8. Yes. This is like example 1 on p. 378: the estimate is based on a simple random sample.

9. This is not the right SE. The bank has mixed up 73¢ with 73%. (The right way to figure the SE for an average will be explained in chapter 23.)

10. Your net gain is like the sum of 100 draws from a box with 6 tickets marked "$11" and 94 marked "−$1." The average of the box is −$0.28, and the SD is about $2.85. Your net gain will be around −$28, give or take $28 or so.

11. $710/100 = 7.1$, so the two options describe the same event in different words. They are the same.

12. Option (ii) is it. For example, about 95% of the estimates will be right to within 2 SEs, about 99.7% of them will be right to within 3 SEs, and so forth.

13. (i) is irrelevant, (ii) is a histogram for the numbers drawn, and (iii) is a probability histogram for the sum. Reason: (iii) looks like the normal; (ii) looks like a histogram for the contents of the box; (i) would allow 3 and 4 among the draws.

14. In all three cases, the expected value is 500 and the SE is about 16. You know

what is in the box, the expected value and SE can be computed exactly and do not depend on the data. The three chance errors are 29, −16, and 14.

15. (a,b) Estimated from the data as. Here, you do not know the composition of the box; this must be estimated from the data.

Chapter 22. Measuring Employment and Unemployment

1. (a) False (section 4).

   (b) They were outside the labor force (section 3)—going to school, retired, keeping house, etc.

2. False. This is not a simple random sample (section 5).

3. The estimate is 7.0 million, and the estimated SE is 0.1 million (section 5).

4. Not much (section 7).

5. A simple random sample is drawn at random <u>without</u> replacement (p. 340).

6. Drawing without replacement gives a more accurate estimate for the percentage of 1's in the box, because you are sure to get a new ticket on each draw. (For an extreme example, think about 250 draws: drawing without replacement gives a perfect estimate; not so when drawing with replacement.) Also see p. 368.

   Comment. Drawing with replacement leads to easier formulas for the SE. That is why we study it. The square root law is exact for drawing with replacement, and approximate for drawing without replacement. Exercise 6 is asking about the accuracy of the estimate for the percentage of 1's in the box; it is not asking which formula for the SE is easier or more accurate.

7. (a) This is a probability sample (section 19.4).

   (b) This is not a simple random sample. A simple random sample would give you a chance to draw households from all 5 districts, here you only get 2 out of the 5.

   Comment. There is no selection bias, the procedure is fair and impartial, and in fact, every household has the same chance to get into the sample.

8. (a) This is a probability sample (section 19.4).

   (b) This is not a simple random sample. For example, the auditors can't get items 17 and 18 in the same sample: with a simple random sample, they could.

   Comment. This kind of sample is called a *list sample*, or a *systematic sample*. There is no selection bias, the procedure is fair and impartial, and in fact, every item has the same chance to get into the sample. List samples are easier to draw than simple random samples, and for many purposes they work just fine. You have to be a little careful in figuring the SE, though; and it's better to use several random starts than one.

9. No, because of response bias. The attitude of the interviewers could well affect the responses. (And in this example, it did.)

10. The total of the numbers tossed is like the sum of 200 draws from the box

    $\boxed{1\ 2\ 3\ 4\ 5\ 6}$.

    The average of the box is 3.5, so the total should be around

    $200 \times 3.5 = 700$.

    Boyd is giving us the old razzle dazzle.

11. (a) (i)   (b) (ii)   (c) (ii) (iii)

    Comment. The expected value of the *sample percentage* equals the *population percentage*. This is so even after the sample is drawn—the expected value is sort of the average over all possible samples, not just the particular sample you happened to draw. In the frequency theory, it is a mistake to say that the expected value of the *population percentage* equals the *sample percentage*. See section 21.3.

12. (a) True.

    (b) True.

    (c) False, the normal curve will not work here, the data are too skewed. (For example, the percentage cannot be negative, but $1.04 - 1.46 < 0$.)

Chapter 23. *The Accuracy of Averages*

1. The sum of 400 draws will be around $400 \times 100 = 40{,}000$, give or take

   $\sqrt{400} \times 20 = 400$ or so.

   The average of 400 draws will be around 100, give or take 1 or so.

   (a) The chance is almost 100%.

   (b) The range is "expected value $\pm$ 1 SE," so the chance is about 68%.

   Moral: the SE and the SD are different.

2. (a) True. That's what the SE does for you (pp. 417, 422).

   (b) True. The 68%-confidence interval is "sample average $\pm$ SE for average."

   (c) False (p. 417).

3. Model: there is a box with 50,000 tickets, one for each household in the town. The ticket shows the commute distance for the head of household. The data are like 1000 draws from the box. The SD of the box is unknown, but can be estimated by the SD of the data, as 9.0 miles. The SE for the sum of the draws is estimated as $\sqrt{1000} \times 9 \approx 285$ miles, and the SE for the average is estimated as $285/1000 \approx 0.3$ miles.

   (a) The average commute distance of all 50,000 heads of households in the town is estimated as 8.7 miles; this estimate is likely to be off by 0.3 miles or so.

   (b) 8.7 miles $\pm$ 0.6 miles.

Comment. The normal curve is used to approximate the probability histogram for the sample average, not the histogram for the data; the data are skewed, with a long right hand tail.

4. Can't be done with the information given. This is a simple random sample of households, but a cluster sample of people. The cluster is the household, and people in a household are likely to be similar with respect to commuting. For example, if a household is far from the center of town, all the occupants are likely to have a long commute. The SE is going to be bigger than the SE for a simple random sample of 2500 persons: section 22.5.

5. Model: there is a box with 50,000 tickets, one for each household in the town. The ticket is marked 1 if the head of household commutes by car; otherwise, 0. The data are like 1000 draws from the box. The fraction of 1's in the box is unknown, but can be estimated by the fraction in the sample, as 0.721. On this basis, the SD of the box is estimated as $\sqrt{0.721 \times 0.279} \approx 0.45$. The SE for the number of 1's in 1000 draws is estimated as $\sqrt{1000} \times 0.45 \approx 14$. The SE for the percentage of 1's is 14/1000, or 1.4%. The percentage of 1's in the box is estimated as 72.1%, give or take 1.4% or so. The 95%-confidence interval is $72.1\% \pm 2.8\%$.

Comment. We have a simple random sample of households, and are making an inference about households.

6. (a) Can't be done, you would need to use the half sample method (section 22.5).

   (b) $SE \approx 1$.

7. Option (iii) is it, this is a sample of convenience (p. 424).

8. (a) True: the interval is "average $\pm$ SE."

   (b) True: section 21.3.

   (c) The data don't follow the normal curve, but the 68% might be right; you need the data to tell. (To see that the data don't follow the curve: enrollments can't be negative, but the SD was a lot bigger than the average, so there must have been a long right hand tail.)

   (d) False: 325 is not the SD. (The data aren't normal, which is another problem.)

   (e) False. The normal curve is being used on the probability histogram for the sample average, not the data (pp. 411 and 418–19).

9. 1.7 ± 0.1.

10. (a) True: the SE is estimated from the sample data, as on p. 416.

    (b) False. There is no such thing as a 95%-confidence interval for the *sample average*, you know the sample average. It's the population average that you have to worry about (pp. 385–86).

    (c) True.

(d) False. This confuses the SD with the SE. And it's ridiculous, because a household must have a whole number of persons (1, or 2, or 3, and so forth).

(e) False. For instance, if household size followed the normal curve, there would be many households with a negative number of occupants; we're not ready for that.

(f) True. See pp. 411 and 418–19. Even though household size does not follow the normal curve, you can still use the normal curve to approximate the probability histogram for the sample average.

11. There is too much spread in the histogram: the SE for the average is only about 0.3, there is a lot of area outside the range EV $\pm$ 3 SE.

12. This is not a 95%-confidence interval: the class is a sample of convenience, not a probability sample.

Chapter 23. Special Review Exercises

1. No. The teachers might have been tempted to put the poorer children into the treatment group. (In fact, this seems to have happened; children in the treatment group were significantly smaller in physical size than the controls, which probably biased the study against the treatment.)

2. No. In badly designed studies of surgery, healthier patients are more likely to be picked for the operation, leaving sicker patients to be the controls. Being a control in a badly designed study may be a marker of illness (section 1.2), but it is unlikely to be a cause of illness.

3. (a) Yes. Other things being equal, the drinkers will have higher rates of oral cancer than the non-drinkers, due to the alcohol.

   (b) Option (ii) is right: section 2.5.

4. (a) Yes.

   (b) Yes: we're looking at people who died in 2005. The older ones were born earlier, and are more likely to be right handed.

   (c) The data don't distinguish between (a) and (b), and don't tell you much.

5. Choose (iii). The salary data have a long right hand tail, the average is bigger than the median. The total of a list is

   number of entries $\times$ the average.

   The total cannot be computed from the median.

6. 10 years. If the SD were 1 year or 2 years, a lot of people would be more than 5 SDs from average. If the SD were 25 years, hardly anybody would be more than 1 SD from average.

7. Negative: as chlorophyll concentration becomes bigger, the water gets murkier, and Secchi depth becomes smaller.

8. Yes.

9. Guess 570, using the regression method. You have about a 68% chance to be right to within 1 r.m.s. error, which is about 86 points.

10. The scatter diagram is sketched below. The families where the husband is about $5'\,4'' = 64''$ tall are in the vertical strip. For these husbands to be shorter than their wives, the wife must be taller than $64''$. In this strip, the average height of the wives is $62.1''$ (the new average), and the SD is $2.4''$ (the new SD). The wives have to be taller than $64''$, that is, more than 0.8 new SDs above the new average. The percentage is about the area under the normal curve to the right of 0.8, that is, 21%.

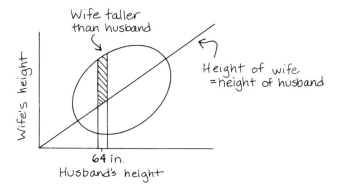

11. (a) 0.25. This line is the regression line for predicting wife's income from husband's (section 10.2).

   (b) The estimate is likely to be too high. You need to use the other line, for predicting husband from wife (section 10.5).

12. Something is wrong. Both lines are too shallow to estimate the average of x given y. (The lighter line is the regression line for y on x; the heavier line is the SD line.)

13. The chance of getting neither an ace nor a king is
   $$44/52 \times 43/51 \times 42/50 \times 41/49 \times 40/48 \approx 42\%.$$
   The answer is $100\% - 42\% = 58\%$.

14. Not possible with information given. You need to know how many people got perfect scores on both midterms.

15. For (a, b, c), the answer is

$$\binom{5}{3}\left(\frac{1}{6}\right)^3\left(\frac{5}{6}\right)^2 = \frac{250}{7776} \approx 3\%$$

16. False. Option (i) has chance $1 - (37/38)^{15} \approx 33\%$, while option (ii) has chance $1 - (37/38)^{30} \approx 55\%$. This is like de Méré (section 14.3).

17. The total is like the sum of 20 draws from the box $\boxed{1\ 0\ 0\ 0\ 0\ 1}$. The average of this new box is 0.33, and the SD is 0.47 by the shortcut (section 17.4). The total will be around $20 \times 0.33 \approx 7$, give or take $\sqrt{20} \times 0.47 \approx 2$ or so.

18. If a student answers at random, the score is like the sum of 50 draws from the box $\boxed{2\ -1\ -1}$. The average of this box is 0, and the SD is 1.41 by the shortcut (section 17.4). The EV for the sum of the draws is $50 \times 0 = 0$; the SE is $\sqrt{50} \times 1.41 \approx 10$. The score will be around 0, give or take 10 or so.

     (a) A cutoff of 50 is 5 SEs, the chance is zilch.

     (b) A cutoff of 10 is 1 SE, the chance is about 16%.

19. The histogram for the data will get closer and closer to the probability histogram for the number of heads in 100 tosses of a coin (section 18.2). This probability histogram is not the normal curve—although it's close (chapter 18, figure 3). Also see pp. 326–27.

20. (a) The normal approximation will be too low, because the curve is lower than the probability histogram at 90.

     (b) The approximation will be about right, because the highs and lows cancel.

21. The number of heads in each group should be around 50, give or take 5 or so; and the groups are independent. Option (i) is right. With (ii), the number of heads is more like 25. With (iii), there is a strong negative correlation from group to group. And with (iv), the SD is more like 10.

22. The EV is 40% and the SE is 2.2% in both parts of the problem. For instance, the SE for the number of blues is $\sqrt{500} \times \sqrt{0.4 \times 0.6} \approx 11$, so the SE for the percentage of blues among the draws is 11/500 or 2.2%. It is a mistake to use the sample fractions when the contents of the box are given.

     (a) The observed value is 218/500 or 43.6%; the chance error is 3.6%.

     (b) The observed value is 191/500 or 38.2%; the chance error is −1.8%.

23. Option (ii) is right. The top histogram is symmetric, the bottom one is skewed. If Box A and Box B were the same, the two histograms would have to be the same (in standard units). See p. 411, and exercise 8 on p. 414.

24. (a) True (section 18.5).

     (b) False. The histogram for the numbers in the box does not change, and could have any shape—depending on how the box was set up in the first place.

     (c) False. The histogram for the draws gets more and more like the histogram for the numbers in the box. You have to distinguish between (i) the probability histogram for the sum of the draws, and (ii) the histogram for the draws as data.

     (d) False (p. 323).

     (e) True.

25. How did they pick the 5 employees? Quite a lot of bias could come in at this stage.

26. The number of blacks in the sample should be around 26, give or take 4.4 or so. The chance of getting 8 or fewer is nearly 0. These jurors were not chosen at random, whatever the Supreme Court thought at the time.

27. (a) 10.8%.

    (b) 1.4%.

    (c) The range from 8.0% to 13.6% is a 95% confidence interval for the percentage of independents among all registered voters in Hayward.

28. This is a cluster sample, so you can't compute the SE from the information given (section 22.5).

29. (i) is the histogram for the numbers drawn: it looks like (iii), but is a little off due to chance error.
    (ii) is the probability histogram for the average of the draws; it is starting to look like the normal curve, but is still a little irregular (there are only 20 draws).
    (iii) is the histogram for the contents of the box: there are exactly as many 2's as 4's, and twice as many 1's as 2's.

30. False. Accuracy in estimated percentages depends mainly on the sample size, not the population size (section 20.4).

Part VII. Chance Models

Chapter 24. A Model for Measurement Error

1. Model: each measurement equals the exact elevation, plus a draw from the error box. The tickets in the box average out to 0. Their SD is unknown, but can be estimated by the SD of the data, as 30 inches. The SE for the sum of the 25 measurements is estimated as $\sqrt{25} \times 30 = 150$ inches. The SE for the average is estimated as $150/25 = 6$ inches.

    (a) 81,411 inches, 6 inches.

    (b) True.

    (c) False. You don't need a confidence interval for the *sample average*, you know the sample average. It's the elevation of the mountain that needs to be estimated.

    (d) False. This mixes up SD and SE.

    (e) False, same issue.

    (f) False; see exercise 8 on p. 421.

2. (a) The probability histogram for the average of the draws follows the curve.

    (b) The histogram for the data doesn't follow the curve.

3. $299{,}774 \pm 0.6$ km/sec.

4. The SD of the distance measurements.

5. If they got the length wrong (as they must have, at least by a little), there is a bias in the speed measurements.

6. False. The average for 2005 is known, a confidence interval is not needed. At a more basic level, the Gauss model does not apply (example 4 on p. 446).

7. Use the SD of the old data, 18 micrograms (example 5 on p. 451). The 95%-interval is 78.1 ± 5.1 micrograms above 1 kilogram.

8. The data are like 100 draws made at random with replacement from a box. The average of the box is about 58 seconds, and the SD is about 2 seconds. The total execution time is like the sum of 100 draws from the box. This will be about $100 \times 58 = 5800$ seconds, give or take $\sqrt{100} \times 2 = 20$ seconds or so.

9. (a) Model: the weights of the sticks are drawn at random from a box. The average of the box is 4 ounces, and the SD is 0.05 ounces. The weight of a package is like the sum of 4 draws. The expected value is $4 \times 4 = 16.0$ ounces. The SE for the sum is $\sqrt{4} \times 0.05 = 0.1$ ounces. The answer: 16 ounces, 0.1 ounces.

   (b) The total weight of 100 packages is like the sum of 400 draws from the box. The expected value is $400 \times 4 = 1600$ ounces $= 100$ pounds. The SE for the sum is $\sqrt{400} \times 0.05 = 1$ ounce. The total weight will be 100 pounds, give or take 1 ounce or so. The range "100 pounds ± 2 ounces" is "expected value ± 2 SE," so the chance is about 95%.

10. False. You use the curve on the probability histogram for the average, not the histogram for the data (pp. 418–19).

11. This procedure invites bias. It would be better to make the measurements some prespecified number of times, and then take the average. Of course, if something went wrong during the measurement process, it might be okay to exclude the result.

Chapter 25. Chance Models in Genetics

1. *First line.* The yellow parent must be y/y. The green parent must be g/y, else, all progeny would be green.

   Second line. Both parents must be g/y, else no yellow progeny.

   Third line. Both parents are y/y.

   Fourth line. The yellow parent is y/y. The green parent must be g/g, else there would be yellow progeny.

   Fifth line. One parent must be g/g, else there would be yellow progeny; the other parent can be g/g or g/y.

2. Genetic model: one gene-pair, with two variants, smooth (s) dominant and wrinkled (w) recessive. Crossing s/w with s/w produces smooth with probability 3/4, wrinkled with probability 1/4. Mendel had $5474 + 1850 = 7324$ plants. The number of smoothies is like the sum of 7324 draws from the box $\boxed{1\ 1\ 1\ 0}$.

The expected value is $7324 \times 3/4 = 5493$. He was off by $5493 - 5474 = 19$. The standard error is $\sqrt{7324} \times \sqrt{3/4 \times 1/4} \approx 37$. The chance is about 38%.

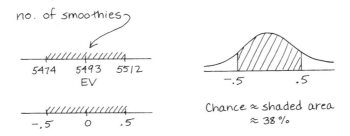

3. Genetic model: one gene-pair, with two variants, early (e) and late (l). e/e is early, l/l is late and e/l is intermediate. So intermediate × intermediate should give about 25% early, 50% intermediate, 25% late. With 2500 plants from this cross, the number of intermediates is like the sum of 2500 draws from the box $\boxed{1 \ 0}$. The expected number is 1250, the SE is 25, and the chance is about 2.5%.

4. (a) No. The man's father contributed the Y-chromosome, and this has nothing to do with baldness.

   (b) Yes. The mother got one X chromosome from her father (the man's maternal grandfather), and may have passed it on to the man.

5. (a) No. The child will have at least one A.

   (b) Yes, if both parents are A/a and the child gets a from each parent.

   (c) No. Both parents are a/a, so the child will be a/a too.

Part VIII. Tests of Significance

Chapter 26. Tests of Significance

1. (a) True (p. 479).

   (b) False. The null says it's chance, the alternative says it's real (pp. 477–78).

2. (a) The data are like 3800 draws made at random with replacement from the box $\boxed{?? \ 0\text{'s} \quad ?? \ 1\text{'s}}$, with 1 = red.

   (b) Null: the fraction of 1's in the box is 18/38, or 47.4%.
   Alt: the fraction of 1's in the box is more than 18/38.

   (c) The expected number of reds (computed using the null) is 1800. The SD of the box (also computed using the null) is nearly 0.5, so the SE for the number of reds is $\sqrt{3800} \times 0.5 \approx 31$. So $z = (\text{obs} - \text{exp})/\text{SE} = (1890 - 1800)/31 \approx 2.9$, and $P \approx 2/1000$.

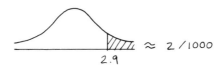

(d) Yes.

Comments. (i) This problem is about the number of reds. In the formula for the z-statistic, *obs, exp,* and *SE* all refer to the number of reds. The expected, as always, is computed from the null. In this problem, the null gives the composition of the box, so the SD is computed from the null; it is not estimated from the data (p. 485).

(ii) This problem, and several others below, can be done using one-sided or two-sided tests. The distinction does not matter here; it is discussed in chapter 29.

3. Null hypothesis: the data are like 200 draws from the box $\boxed{1\ 1\ 1\ 0}$, with 1 = blue and 0 = white. The expected number of blues is 150, and the SE is about 6, so $z = (obs - exp)/SE = (142 - 150)/6 \approx -1.3$ and P $\approx$ 10%. This is marginal, could be chance.

4. The TA's null: the scores in his section are like 30 draws at random from a box containing all 900 scores. (There is little difference between drawing with or without replacement, because the box is so big.) The null hypothesis specifies the average and the SD of the box, 63 and 20. The EV for the average of the draws is 63, and the SE is 3.65. So $z = (obs - exp)/SE = (55 - 63)/3.65 \approx -2.2$, and $P \approx 1\%$. The TA's defense is not good.

5. The box has one ticket for each freshman at the university, showing how many hours per week that student spends at parties. So there are about 3000 tickets in the box. The data are like 100 draws from the box. The null hypothesis says that the average of the box is 7.5 hours. The alternative says that the average is less than 7.5 hours. The observed value for the sample average is 6.6 hours. The SD of the box is not known, but can be estimated from the data as 9 hours. On this basis, the SE for the sample average is estimated as 0.9 hours. Then $z = (obs - exp)/SE \approx (6.6 - 7.5)/0.9 = -1$. The difference looks like chance.

6. (a) In the best case for Judge Ford, we are tossing a coin 350 times, and asking for the chance of getting 102 heads or fewer. The expected number of heads is 175 and the SE is a little over 9, so $z \approx (102 - 175)/9 \approx -8$. The chance is about 0.

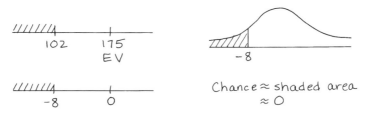

    (b) 100 draws are made at random without replacement from a box with 102 1's and 248 0's, where 1 = woman and 0 = man. The expected number of 1's is 29. If the draws are made with replacement, the SE for the number of 1's is $\sqrt{100} \times \sqrt{0.29 \times 0.71} \approx 4.54$. The correction factor is

$$\sqrt{\frac{350 - 100}{350 - 1}} \approx 0.846.$$

The SE for the number, when drawing without replacement, is

$0.846 \times 4.54 \approx 3.8$.

So $z \approx (9 - 29)/3.8 \approx -5.3$. The chance is about 0.

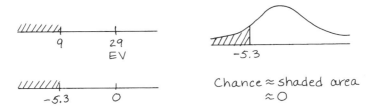

(c) Judge Ford was not choosing at random; he was excluding women.

Comment. After Hans Zeisel made a statistical analysis of Judge Ford's procedures, the percentage of women jurors went up quite dramatically; see note 15 to chapter 26.

7. Disagree. There are $580 + 442 = 1022$ subjects. With a coin, the expected number in the control group is 511, and the SE is about 16, so the chance of getting 442 or fewer in the control group is practically 0. Both patients and doctors know that if you turn up on an odd day of the month, you get the therapy. There may be a considerable temptation to enroll more patients on odd days, and that seems to be what happened.

   Comment. The danger is that the patients enrolled on the odd days will be different from the ones enrolled on the even days. For example, the doctors may tend to enroll relatively healthy patients—who need the therapy less—on the even days. If the control group starts off healthier than the treatment group, the study is biased against the treatment. Tossing a coin is wiser.

8. Model: there is one ticket in the box for each person in the county, age 18 and over. The ticket shows that person's educational level. The data are like 1000 draws from the box.

   > Null: the average of the box is 13 years.
   > Alt: the average of the box isn't 13 years.

   The expected value for the average of the draws is 13 years, based on the null. The SD of the box is unknown (there is no reason the spread in the county should equal the spread in the nation), but can be estimated as 5 years—the SD of the data. On this basis, the SE for the sample average is estimated as 0.16 years. The observed value for the sample average is 14 years, so

   $z = (\text{obs} - \text{exp})/\text{SE} = (14 - 13)/0.16 \approx 6$,

   and $P \approx 0$. This is probably a rich, suburban county, where the educational level would be higher than average.

9. Something is wrong. The EV for the sum is 20; the SE for the sum is 4. The average of 144 sums should be around 20; the SE for the average is 0.33. The observed value is 3.4 SEs away from expected. That is too many SEs.

You can also get the EV and SE another way: the average of 144 sums is like the sum of $144 \times 100 = 14,400$ draws from the original box, divided by 144.

10. Null: the 3 Sunday numbers are like 3 draws made at random (without replacement) from a box containing all 25 numbers in the table. The average of these numbers is nearly 436, and their SD is just about 40. The EV for the average is 436, and the SE is 22; we are using the correction factor here. The 3 Sunday numbers average about 357, so

$$z = (\text{obs} - \text{exp})/\text{SE} = (357 - 436)/22 \approx -3.6,$$

and $P \approx 2/10,000$.

Comments. (i) Many deliveries are induced, and some are surgical, so obstetricians really can influence the timing.

(ii) In all, there are $25!/(3! \times 22!) = 2300$ samples of size 3. The 3 Sunday numbers are 344, 377, 351. The number for Saturday, August 6, is also 377; and all the other numbers in the table are larger. Therefore, exactly 2 samples have an average equal to the Sunday average, and no sample average is smaller. The exact significance probability is $2/2300 \approx 9/10,000$, compared to $2/10,000$ from the curve.

Sundays are for golf.

11. (a) The box has one ticket for each household in Atlanta in June 2003. If the income is over \$52,000, the ticket is marked 1; otherwise, 0. The null hypothesis says that the percentage of 1's in the box is 50%; the alternative, that percentage of 1's in the box is bigger than 50%. The data are like 750 draws from the box.

(b) The SE for the number of 1's in the sample is $\sqrt{750} \times \sqrt{0.50 \times 0.50} \approx 13.7$; the SE for the percentage of 1's in the sample is 13.7/750, or 1.83%. So $z = 6/1.83 \approx 3.3$, and P is very small.

(c) Median household income went up.

12. (a) There are 59 pairs, and in 52 of them, the treatment animal has a heavier cortex. On the null hypothesis, the expected number is $59 \times 0.5 = 29.5$ and the SE is $\sqrt{59} \times 0.5 \approx 3.84$. So 52 is nearly 6 SEs above average, and the chance is close to 0. Inference: treatment made the cortex weigh more.

(b) The average is about 36 milligrams and the SD is about 31 milligrams. The SE for the average is 4 milligrams, so $z = 36/4 = 9$ and $P \approx 0$. (This is like the tax example in section 1.) Inference: treatment made the cortex weigh more.

(c) This blinds the person doing the dissection to the treatment status of the animal. It is a good idea, because it prevents bias; otherwise, the technician might skew the results to favor the research hypothesis.

Chapter 27. More Tests for Averages

1. No. The expected number of positives is 250, and the SE is $\sqrt{500} \times 0.5 \approx 11$. The observed number is 2.4 SEs above the expected. (Here, a one-sample test is appropriate.)

2. (a) The SE for the difference is 5.9%, so $z = 2.4/5.9 \approx 0.4$; looks like chance.

(b) The SE for the difference is 1.8; the observed difference is 4.9; so $z = 4.9/1.8 \approx 2.7$ and $P \approx 0.3$ of 1%. The difference looks real.

Comment. There is more information in the sample average than in the number of positive terms, at least for this example.

3. There are two samples, you need to make a two-sample z-test. Model: there are two boxes. The 2005 box has a ticket for each person in the population, marked 1 for those who would rate clergymen "very high or high," and 0 otherwise. The 2005 data are like 1000 draws from the 1985 box. The 2000 box is set up the same way. The null hypothesis says that the percentage of 1's in the 2005 box is the same as in the 2000 box. The alternative hypothesis says that the percentage of 1's in the 2005 box is smaller than the percentage of 1's in the 2000 box.

The SD of the 2005 box is estimated from the data as $\sqrt{0.54 \times 0.46} \approx 0.50$. On this basis, the SE for the 2005 number is $\sqrt{1000} \times 0.50 \approx 16$: the number of respondents in the sample who rate clergymen "very high or high" is 540, and the chance error in that number is around 16. Convert the 15 to percent, relative to 1000. The SE for the 2005 percentage is estimated as 1.6%. Similarly, the SE for the 2000 percentage is about 1.5%.

The SE for the difference is computed from the square root law (p. 502) as

$$\sqrt{1.6^2 + 1.5^2} \approx 2.2\%.$$

The observed difference is $54 - 60 = -6\%$. On the null hypothesis, the expected difference is 0%. So $z = (\text{obs} - \text{exp})/\text{SE} = -6/2.2 \approx -2.7$, and $P \approx 3/1000$. The difference is real. What the cause is, the test cannot say.

Comment. Either a one-sided or a two-sided test can be used. Here, the distinction is not so relevant: for discussion, see chapter 29.

4. You need more information. The method of section 2 does not apply because you do not have two independent samples. The method of sections 3–4 does not apply because you observe two responses for each person. See p.517.

5. This is like the radiation-surgery example in section 4. Each subject has two possible responses, one to item A and one to item B. The investigators only observe one of the two, chosen at random. To make the test, pretend you have two independent random samples. With item A, the percentage who answer "yes" is 46%; the SE for this percentage is 3.5%. With item B, the percentage is 88% and the SE is 2.4%. The difference between the percentages is $46\% - 88\% = -42\%$. The SE for the difference is conservatively estimated as $\sqrt{3.5^2 + 2.4^2} \approx 4.2\%$. So $z = -42/4.2 = -10$. The framing of the question makes a difference. That is what the experiment tells you.

6. This is just like the previous exercise. In the calculator group, 7.2% get the right answer; in the pencil-and-paper group, 23.6%. The SEs are 1.6% and 2.7%. The difference between the percentages is -16.4%, and the SE for the difference is conservatively estimated as $\sqrt{1.6^2 + 2.7^2} \approx 3.1\%$. So $z = -16.4/3.1 \approx -5$, and $P \approx 0$. The difference is real. (Students who used the calculator seemed to forget what the arithmetic was all about.)

7. (a) This is like the radiation-surgery example in section 4. (Also see review exercises 5 and 6 above.) The SE for the treatment percent is 2.0%. The SE for the control pecent is 4.0%. The SE for the difference is 4.5%. The observed difference, 1.1%, is only 0.24 of an SE. This could easily be due to chance. Income support was a good idea that didn't work.

   (b) This is like example 4. The SE for the treatment average is 0.7 weeks; for the control average, 1.4 weeks; for the difference, 1.6 weeks. The observed difference is -7.5 weeks. So $z = -7.5/1.6 \approx 4.7$ and $P \approx 0$. The difference is real. Income support makes the released prisoners work less, which might explain the findings in part (a).

8. The data can be summarized as follows:

	Prediction Request	Request only
Predicts	22/46	NA
Agrees	14/46	2/46

(a) This is like the radiation-surgery example in section 4. The two percentages are 47.8% and 4.4%. The SEs are about 7.4% and 3.0%, respectively. The difference is 43.4% and the SE for the difference is 8%. So $z = 43.4/8 \approx 5.4$ and $P \approx 0$. The difference is real. People overestimate their willingness to do volunteer work.

(b) The two percentages are 30.4% and 4.4%. The SEs are about 6.8% and 3.0%, respectively. The difference is 26% and the SE for the difference is 7.4%. So $z = 26/7.4 = 3.5$ and $P \approx 2/10,000$. The difference is real. Asking people to predict their behavior changes what they will do.

(c) Here, a two-sample z-test is not legitimate. There is only one sample, and two responses for each person in the sample. Both responses are observed, so the method of section 4 does not apply. The responses are correlated, so the method of example 3 does not apply. See p.517.

Comment. In parts (a) and (b), the number of draws is small relative to the number of tickets in the box. So there is little difference between drawing with or without replacement, and little dependence between the treatment and control averages. See pp.510, 517.

9. This is like the radiation-surgery example in section 4. In the positive group, the percentage accepted is $28/53 \times 100\% \approx 52.8\%$; in the negative group, 14.8%. The SEs are 6.9% and 4.8%. The difference is 38% and the SE for the difference is 8.4%. So $z = 38/8.4 \approx 4.5$ and $P \approx 0\%$. There is a big difference between the two groups, and the difference cannot be explained by chance. Journals prefer the positive articles.

10. This test is not legitimate. There is dependence between the first-borns and second-borns.

11. (i) The expected value for the difference between the average score in the 2004 sample and the average score in the 1990 sample equals the expected value for the average score in the 2004 sample, minus the expected value for the average score in the 1990 sample. (ii) The expected value for the average score in the 2004 sample is the average of the 2004 box; likewise, the expected value for the average score in the 1990 sample is the average of the 1990 box. (iii) If you put the previous points together, the expected value for the difference between the averages of the two samples equals the difference between the averages of the two boxes. (iv) The null hypothesis says that the difference between the averages of the two boxes is 0. That is why 0 is the right benchmark in the numerator of the z-statistic.

Chapter 28. The Chi-Square Test

1. (a) (i) (b) (iii). See exercises 3–6 on pp.539–40.

2. Use the method of sections 1–2.

Observed	Expected
1	17.6
10	30.1
16	7.4
35	6.9

$\chi^2 \approx 150$ on 3 degrees of freedom, so $P \approx 0$ and option (ii) is right.

Comments. (i) Judges prefer well-educated grand jurors.
(ii) The expecteds do not have to be whole numbers. For instance, if you roll a die 100 times, the expected number of aces is 16.666 . . . .

3. Use the method of section 4. The expecteds are as follows (row and column sums are a bit off due to rounding).

	Married	Widowed, divorced, or separated	Never married
Employed	772.0	103.3	221.7
Unemployed	66.2	8.9	19.0
Not in labor force	28.9	3.9	8.3

$\chi^2 \approx 14.2$ on 4 degrees of freedom, which is off the end of the table. By computer, $P \approx 0.7$ of 1%. This is not chance variation. The married men do better at getting jobs. (Or, men with jobs do better at getting married: the χ^2-test will not tell you which is the cause and which is the effect.)

4. (a) Chance: it's a probability histogram.
    (b) The chance that $5 \le \chi^2 < 5.2$, where χ^2 is computed from 60 rolls of a fair die.
    (c) The chance that $5 \le \chi^2 < 5.2$ is bigger than the chance that $4.8 \le \chi^2 < 5$. (The block is bigger.)
    (d) 10%.

    Comment. The exact probability distribution of χ^2, with 60 rolls, is quite irregular. As the number of rolls goes up, the histogram gets closer to the curve. See p.41 of this manual.

5. (a) With 10 degrees of freedom, P will be bigger. Reason: that curve has more area to the right of 15.
    (b) The P-value is bigger when $\chi^2 = 15$. Reason: the area under the curve to the right of 15 is bigger than the area to the right of 20.

6. Use the method of section 3. The observed frequencies are too close to the expected ones for comfort: $\chi^2 \approx 2$ on 10 degrees of freedom, so $P < 1\%$ (left tail); by computer, $P \approx 0.4$ of 1%. This individual seems to have very good control over the dice. Maybe you should decline his invitation to play craps.

7. Use the method of sections 1–2: $\chi^2 \approx 0.2$ on 2 degrees of freedom, $P \approx 90\%$, a good fit.

8. Make a χ^2-test, as in sections 1–2. We are interested in the chances, not just the average: $\chi^2 \approx 2.6$ on 5 degrees of freedom, $P \approx 75\%$, a good fit.

9. Use the method of section 4. The expecteds are as follows:

	20–24	25–29
Never married	34.9	32.1
Married	25.5	23.5
W/D/S	3.6	3.4

$\chi^2 \approx 17$ on 2 degrees of freedom; by computer, $P < 2/1000$. This is not chance variation. It takes time to get married, especially in Montana.

10. (a) Use the method of section 4 to compute χ^2.

	Observed		Expected	
	Protestant	Catholic	Protestant	Catholic
Acquitted	8	27	6.56	28.44
Convicted	7	38	8.44	36.56

	Obs − Exp	
	Protestant	Catholic
Acquitted	1.44	−1.44
Convicted	−1.44	1.44

Now

$$\chi^2 = \frac{1.44^2}{6.56} + \frac{1.44^2}{8.44} + \frac{1.44^2}{28.44} + \frac{1.44^2}{36.56}$$
$$= 1.44^2 \times \left(\frac{1}{6.56} + \frac{1}{8.44} + \frac{1}{28.44} + \frac{1}{36.56}\right) = 0.69$$

and $P \approx 60\%$. The mistake, apparently, was to compute

$$1.44^2 \div \left(\frac{1}{6.56} + \frac{1}{8.44} + \frac{1}{28.44} + \frac{1}{36.56}\right) = 6.22.$$

(b) Presumably, the defense was thinking that accused persons are convicted independently, with a common probability—except that there is one probability for Catholics and another for Protestants. This model does not seem well related to the criminal justice system, where the facts vary from one case to the next, and some cases involve multiple defendants.

Chapter 29. A Closer Look at Tests of Significance

1. (a) True (p. 547). (b) False (pp. 552–53). (c) False (p. 545).

Of course, $P = 4.7\%$ gives you "statistical significance," and improves the odds of journal publication.

2. Question (i): see p. 562.

3. False. You have to take the sample size into account too. For example, suppose the first investigator gets an average of 52, and the second one gets an average

of 51. The first investigator gets $z = (52 - 50)/1 = 2$ and $P \approx 5\%$. The second investigator gets $z = (51 - 50)/0.33 = 3$ and $P \approx 0.3$ of 1%. (The P-values are two-sided.)

4. Yes: data snooping (p. 547).

5. It is hard to make sense out of "statistical significance" here, because there is no reasonable chance model for the data. The inner planets do not form a sample, they are the inner planets; similarly for the outer ones. (See exercise 2 on pp. 558–59; but see note 20 to chapter 29.)

6. There may be a big effect which is poorly estimated (pp. 552–53). Also, there may be problems in setting up a box model here.

7. The concept of statistical significance does not apply very well, because the data are for the whole population, rather than a sample (p. 556). The difference is practically significant. The center of population is shifting to the West, and that makes a lot of difference to the economy and to the political balance of the country.

8. (a) The question makes sense: the data are from probability samples.

   (b) No. You need to use the half-sample method (section 22.5).

   (c) Yes. Use the method of example 3 on p. 505. The SE for the 2005 sample percentage is 0.22 of 1%, and the SE for 1985 is about the same. The SE for the difference is 0.31 of 1%, so $z = 9/0.31 \approx 29$, and $P \approx 0$. This difference is off the chance scale. Increasing participation by women in the labor force is of great practical importance too.

9. (a) The question makes sense, and the difference in attitudes is important. (This is a practical judgment, not a statistical one.)

   (b) The question makes sense, because the data are based on probability samples; but to answer it, you need to use the half-sample method (section 22.5).

   (c) Now this is like example 3 on p. 505. The SE for the 2000 percentage is 1.4%; for 1970, the SE is 1.5%. The difference is 38%, and the SE for the difference is 2.1%, so $z = 38/2.1 \approx 18$ and $P \approx 0$.

10. $P \approx 5.9\%$ is pretty weak evidence; two-tailed, $P \approx 11.8\%$, which is worse. Even to get these P-values, some data-snooping was needed. The argument is not good.

    Comment. There were also serious problems with the model; see note 38 to chapter 29.

11. The question makes sense, but cannot be answered with the information given: you observe two correlated responses for each subject (p. 517).

12. The conclusion (there are genetic differences among ethnic groups) seems right, but the quotation is overheated.

(i) P-values may be objective, but the 5% line is somewhat arbitrary (pp. 545–46).

(ii) Differences which are statistically significant can be due to chance (p. 547); the P-value only tells you that chance has to work hard to make such a big difference.

(iii) A "statistically significant" difference may be practically insignificant (pp. 552–53).

Chapter 29. Special Review Exercises

1. (a) This is an observational study. It is the prisoners themselves who decide whether to stay in the program or drop out.

    (b) The treatment group consists of the prisoners who finish boot camp. The control group consists of those who drop out.

    (c) Those who stayed the course might have been quite different to start with—better motivated, more self-disciplined—than those who dropped out.

    (d) (i) The treatment group consists of all those who volunteer for the program, whether or not they complete it. The control group consists of those who do not volunteer.
    (ii) The recidivism rate in the two groups is similar, suggesting that the program has little effect.
    Comments. (i) If anything, this comparison is biased in favor of treatment, because those who volunteer would seem more likely to succeed in civilian life than those who do not volunteer. (ii) Completion seems to be an effective screening device: prisoners who finish are motivated and have enough self-discipline to go straight when they are released.

    (e) Most completed. The recidivism rate for those who completed is 29%. The rate for those who did not complete is 74%. The rate for the combined group is 36%. If most dropped out, the rate for the combined group would be nearly 74%. On the other hand, if most completed, the rate for the combined group would be nearly 29%—and it is.

    A more exact answer is possible. Let x be the fraction who completed. Then $29x + 74(1 - x) = 36$, so $x \approx 0.84$.

2. Not a good explanation. The comparison is between left handed ball players and right handed players. A confounder would have to be associated with left handedness—among the players—and cause higher mortality rates. Also see the comment on special review exercise 10, chapter 6.
    This study had problems, including a small sample size.

3. False. This is like the graduate admissions study, pp. 17ff. As it turns out, most of the Catholics go to the Secondary Schools, and students in those schools do rather poorly on the proficiency tests.

4. The figure is not a histogram: the class intervals are unequal. If you adjust for the lengths of the intervals, the pattern goes away—as shown by the histogram on the next page. Class intervals include the left endpoint but not the right. For

instance, the rectangle whose base is the interval from 25 to 30 represents the students age 25–29; those age 30 are in the next rectangle. We started the first rectangle at 15, and ended the last one at 75, somewhat arbitrarily. What the histogram shows is that most students are in their early 20s, with a sprinkling of precocious youngsters—and some determined oldsters.

Histogram of ages, special review exercise 4, chapter 29

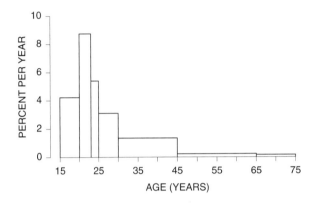

5. The data are cross-sectional not longitudinal. An alternative explanation: death rates are higher among people who drink, smoke, and don't eat breakfast. So, fewer of these people survive past 65 and get interviewed. The conclusion may be right, but doesn't follow from the data.

6. The difference between the 90th and 50th percentiles is bigger. There is a long right hand tail at work.

7. There is a couple where both husband and wife are about 2 years old. There is a man aged 55 married to a 5-year-old. There is a woman aged 30 married to a 5-year-old. And many other odd couples. Something is wrong.

    Comment. For the motivation, see the discussion of review exercise 11 in chapter 11.

8. $y = 0.533x + 1.667$

9. (a) Investigator A gets the higher correlation: B's correlation is attenuated due to restriction of range. (See exercises 4 and 5 on p. 130, exercise 9 on p. 144, exercise set B on pp. 145–46.)

    Comment. In the March 2005 Current Population Survey, the correlations were about 0.31 and 0.23, respectively.

    (b) The "ecological" correlation—for the state averages—will be higher. See section 9.4.

10. Option (iii) is right—regression effect.

11. A first-year GPA of 3.5 is 1 SD above average. Students with this GPA averaged about $r \times 1 - 0.4$ SDs above average in second year, by the regression method.

Sally must have been above average on second-year GPA by about 0.4 SDs, putting her in the 66th percentile.

12. Something is wrong. The r.m.s. error has to be less than the SD.

13. Less than. The diagram is heteroscedastic, with less scatter around the regression line for women with lower educational levels (p. 192).

14. The students who scored 500 on the V-SAT averaged about $0.6 \times 500 + 220 = 520$ on the M-SAT. That is the new average. The new SD is the r.m.s. error of the regression line, which is 80 points. Now $(500 - 520)/80 = -0.25$. The area under the normal curve to the right of -0.25 is about 60%. The answer: about 60% of $50,000 = 0.60 \times 50,000 = 30,000$ students scored better than 500 on the M-SAT.

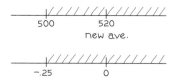

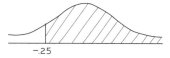

15. (a) $4/52 \times 3/51 \times 2/50 \approx 2/10,000$.

    (b) $48/52 \times 47/51 \times 46/50 \approx 78\%$.

    (c) $36/52 \times 35/51 \times 34/50 \approx 32\%$.

    (d) $100\% - 32\% = 68\%$.

16.
$$\binom{6}{3} \left(\frac{1}{6}\right)^3 \left(\frac{1}{6}\right)^3 = \frac{20}{46,656} \approx \frac{4}{10,000}$$

17. The net gain is like the sum of 100 draws from a box with 18 tickets marked "+\$1," 18 tickets marked "−\$1," and 2 tickets marked "−\$0.50." (These last 2 tickets correspond to 0 and 00, where you only lose half your stake.) The average of this box is $-\$1/38 \approx -\$0.0263$. The expected net gain is $-\$2.63$. The SD of the box—don't use the short-cut—is \$0.980. The SE for the net gain is \$9.80. Now $\$2.63/\$9.80 \approx 0.27$. The answer is about 40%.

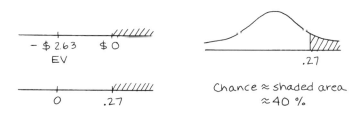

18. Using a telephone survey tends to exclude the homeless or recently homeless. On this basis, the 3% is a little too low.

Comment. People might not want to admit having been homeless; that also makes the 3% too low. On the other hand, if people were homeless, they might remember that as being more recent than it really was. (Vivid experiences tend to be brought forward in memory.) That would make the 3% too high.

19. (a) Each man in the population has had sex with some number of women, perhaps 0. Adding these numbers up gives the total number of female partners for the men. There is a similarly-defined total number of male partners for the women. The two totals must be equal—if a man has a woman as partner, that woman has the man as partner. Since the number of men in the population is about equal to the number of women, the average number of partners must be about the same.

     Comment. Strict equality need not hold—as Laumann points out—although the exceptions seem quite minor. For instance, American men might be more likely than women to have sex while travelling out of the country.

   (b) The total of a list is related to the average not the median, so Laumann seems to have missed the point.

   (c) Lewontin's point is a good one: people in jail, and the homeless, are much more exposed to AIDs than the rest of us. The omission distorts the results in an important way.

   (d) Non-respondents may well behave quite differently from respondents.

20. The number of sample families without cars is like the sum of 1500 draws from a 0–1 box. There is a ticket in the box for each of the 25,000 families in the town, marked 1 (no car) or 0 (owns cars). So, the fraction of 1's in the box is 0.1, and the SD of the box is $\sqrt{0.1 \times 0.9} = 0.3$. The expected value for the sum is $1500 \times 0.1 = 150$. The SE is $\sqrt{1500} \times 0.3 \approx 12$. The number of sample families without cars will be around 150, give or take 12 or so. Now 12 out of 1500 is 0.8 of 1%. The percentage of sample families without cars will be around 10%, give or take 0.8 of 1% or so. The chance is about 80%.

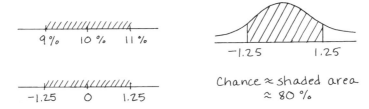

21. Option (i) is right: section 20.4.

22. The town is large, there is not much difference between drawing with or without replacement. Use the method of section 18.4. The number with phones is like the sum of 500 draws from a box with 80 tickets marked "1" and 20 marked "0." The expected number is $500 \times 0.80 = 400$. The SE is $\sqrt{500} \times \sqrt{0.80 \times 0.20} \approx 8.94$. And $0.5/8.94 \approx 0.056$. From the table, the chance is about 4%.

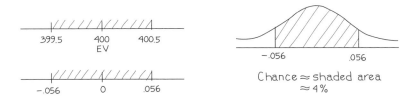

Chance ≈ shaded area
≈ 4%

Comments. (i) By computer, the area under the normal curve between $\pm.056$ is 4.47%.

(ii) You can also use the binomial formula (chapter 15), provided you have a computer to work out the binomial coefficient and the powers:

$$\binom{500}{400}(0.8)^{400}(0.2)^{100} \approx 4.46\%$$

The normal approximation is very good—4.47% vs. 4.46%.

23. (a) Bias; section 19.3.

    (b) A cluster sample is a probability sample, a sample of convenience isn't; sections 19.4, 22.5, 23.4.

    (c) Cluster samples are generally less accurate than simple random samples of the same size, but much cheaper, so they are quite cost effective; section 22.5.

24. False. This is a sample of convenience, not a simple random sample. The formula does not apply (p.424).

25. (a) (i)   (b) (ii)   (c) (ii) (iii)

Comment. The expected value of the *sample average* equals the *population average*. This is so even after the sample is drawn—the expected value is sort of the average over all possible samples, not just the particular sample you happened to draw. In the frequency theory, it is a mistake to say that the expected value of the *population average* equals the *sample average*. See section 21.3 for a similar point about percentages.

26. (a) True: $(488 + 592)/2 = 540$.

    (b) True: just work out the SE and the confidence interval from the SD of 390 and the sample size of 225.

    (c) False. The SD is a large fraction of the average. If the data followed the normal curve, there would be a lot of negative distances travelled.

    (d) True; pp.411, 418–19.

    (e) False. The population average does not have a probability histogram.

    (f) False. If you double the sample size, you cut the SE for the average not by a full factor of 2, but only by $\sqrt{2} \approx 1.4$. The confidence interval will be about $1/1.4 \approx 0.7$ as wide.

Comment. The problem is tacitly assuming that the airline used a symmetric confidence interval.

27. (a) Can't be done with the information given, you have to use the half sample method (section 22.5).

    (b) 0.5 of 1%.

28. Disagree. The SE measures the likely size of the chance error. It does not take bias into account. Therefore, neither does the confidence interval.

29. Option (ii) is it. The half sample method must be used (section 22.5).

30. (a) True.

    (b) False. You can use the variability in the data to estimate the SD of the error box, and then compute a standard error for the average. See part (c).

    (c) True. The SD of the data estimates the SD of the error box, hence, the chance error in a single measurement. The SE for the average can be estimated by the square root law, as in section 24.1.

31. (a) 15, the SD of the measurements.

    (b) $15/\sqrt{25}$, the SE for the average.

32. There is a 25% chance for a chick to be c/c and have white feathers, so the chance of getting 12 chicks out of 24 with colored feathers is

$$\binom{24}{12}(.75)^{12}(.25)^{12} \approx 0.5 \text{ of } 1\%.$$

    You can also use the method of section 18.4, which gives 0.37 of 1%.

33. Model: there is one ticket in the box for each household in the country, marked 1 if the household experienced a burglary within the last 12 months, and 0 otherwise. There are 100 million tickets in this box. The Survey data are like 50,000 draws made at random from the box. (There is essentially no difference between drawing with or without replacement.) If the FBI data are accurate, the percentage of 1's in the box is 2%: this is the null hypothesis. On the null hypothesis, the 3% is higher than the 2% just because of sampling error. The alternative hypothesis: the percentage of 1's in the box is bigger than 2%.

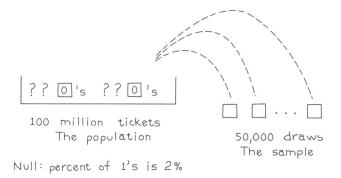

If the null hypothesis is right, the percentage of 1's has an EV of 2%, and the SE is 0.06 of 1%. (The SD of the box should be computed using the 2% specified by the null hypothesis.) The percentage of 1's in the sample is 3%. The difference between 3% and 2% is almost impossible to explain as chance variation: $z \approx 20$. Many burglaries are not reported to the police.

34. (a) True (section 18.4).   (b) False (pp. 480–81).   (c) False (pp. 480–81).

35. Parts (a–d) can be handled like example 4 on p. 508; parts (e–g), like the radiation-surgery example on pp. 512ff. By convention, the "observed difference" is "treatment − control."

   (a) $z = 0.1/0.13 \approx 0.8$ and $P \approx 21\%$. At baseline, the difference between the two groups is well within the range of chance; the randomization worked. (Compare exercise 3 on p. 511.)

   (b) $z = -3.1/0.15 \approx -21$ and $P \approx 0$. The intervention really got the blood pressure to go down.

   (c) $z = 0.3/0.65 \approx 0.46$ and $P \approx 33\%$. At baseline, the difference between the two groups is well within the range of chance; the randomization worked.

   (d) $z = -4.8/0.69 \approx -7$ and $P \approx 0$. The intervention really got the serum cholesterol to go down.

   (e) $z = 0.3/0.87 \approx 0.34$ and $P \approx 36\%$. At baseline, the difference between the two groups is well within the range of chance; the randomization worked.

   (f) $z = -13.3/0.85 \approx -16$ and $P \approx 0$. The intervention really got them to give up smoking.

   (g) The 6-year death rate in the treatment group was 3.28%, compared to 3.40% in control. The SEs are 0.22 of 1% and 0.23 of 1%. The difference is −0.12 of 1%, and the SE for the difference is 0.32 of 1%. So $z = -0.12/0.32 \approx -0.38$ and $P \approx 34\%$. The intervention got the risk factors down, but didn't change the death rate.

   Comments. (i) The sample sizes used in the calculation are at baseline; no adjustment is made for mortality. (This would be minor.)
   (ii) MRFIT was a well-designed, well-conducted study—which came up with answers contradicting the prevailing wisdom. For more cites to the literature on cholesterol, see note 7 to chapter 29.

36. The question makes sense, but cannot be answered with the information given: you have two correlated responses for each subject (p. 517).

37. (a) Can't be done with the information given, the Current Population Survey isn't a simple random sample (chapter 22).

   (b) Use the method of section 28.4.

Obs		Exp		Obs − Exp	
12	34	22.3	23.7	−10.3	10.3
15	17	15.5	16.5	−0.5	0.5
5	2	3.4	3.6	1.6	−1.6
31	14	21.8	23.2	9.2	−9.2

$\chi^2 \approx 18.2$ on 3 degrees of freedom, $P \approx 4/10{,}000$.

Interpretation: women who are less well educated tend not to be in the labor force; women who are better educated are more likely to be in the labor force, and in professional or managerial jobs.

38. The quote is misleading (pp. 480–81). The test tells you the chance of seeing a big difference, given the null hypothesis. It does not tell you the chance that the null hypothesis is right, given the big difference.

39. These investigators seem to have made a number of statistical errors. For one thing, they did lots of tests; data snooping makes P-values hard to interpret (p. 547): even if all their null hypotheses were right, they were almost bound to find some highly significant differences. For another thing, they seem to be thinking that P measures the size of the effect, and it doesn't (pp. 552–53). The effect they estimated is minute: a 100-fold increase in asbestos fiber concentration only increases the risk of lung cancer by a factor of 1.05. Finally, and most important: smoking is a major cause of lung cancer, and the investigators paid no attention to this variable. The argument is weak, and there is no reason to think that asbestos in the water causes lung cancer.

     Comment. See note 52 to chapter 29.

40. (a) The population and the sample are the same, namely, all Dutch men from two-child families who came of military age in the period 1963–66. The estimates and the parameters coincide, because we have data for the whole population.

     (b) The statistical tests do not make much sense, because the data are for a whole population (p. 556). Even if you think of these men as a sample from larger population, why is it anything like a simple random sample?

     Comments. (i) The first-borns and the second-borns would generally be from different families, due to the design.
     (ii) Belmont and Marolla did interesting work, but the tests seem to be largely ceremonial. See note 20 to chapter 19.

Test Results from the First Edition

FREEDMAN-PURVES
DIAGNOSTIC QUIZ

[This test was given to 316 students.]

This is a diagnostic quiz to help us determine the general level of mathematical ability in the class. Many of the skills tested in the quiz will not be used in the course. Your score on this quiz will not affect your grade, but please do your best. If you do not know the answer to a question, do not guess—just leave it blank.

1. 300 is what percent of 2,000?   *[74% got this right.]*

2. A town has 100,000 families; 0.1 of 1% of these families have incomes over $75,000 a year. The number of such families is _____.
    [71% got this right.]

3. There are 100 million eligible voters in the United States. The Gallup poll interviews 5,000 of them. This amounts to one eligible voter out of every _____.   *[61% got this right.]*

4. In the United States, 1 person out of every 200 is in the army, and 8 of every 10,000 are army officers. What percentage of army personnel are officers, or can this be determined from the information given?   *[20% got this right.]*

5. In the United States, 1 person out of every 500 is in the navy, and one-sixth of naval personnel are officers. What fraction of the U.S. population consists of naval officers? Or can this be determined from the information given?   *[27% got this right.]*

6. $\sqrt{100,000}$ is about:

    (i) 30   (ii) 300   (iii) 1,000   (iv) 3,000   (v) can't tell

    [64% got this right.]

7. $\sqrt{17}/17 - 17/\sqrt{17}$.   True   False   Don't Know

    [81% got this right.]   _____   _____   _____

8. $\sqrt{1/2}$ is smaller than $1/2$.

    [41% got this right.]   _____   _____   _____

9. $\sqrt{(2.5)^2 + (3.4)^2} = 2.5 + 3.4$ _____   _____   _____

    [59% got this right.]

10. Solve for x and y, if possible: $x + 3y = 1$, $2x + y = -3$. *[54% got this right.]*

11. A quart of vodka is 40% alcohol. Write a formula for the percentage of alcohol in a mixture of V quarts of vodka and J quarts of orange juice. *[15% got this right.]*

12. This year John's mother is exactly three times as old as he is. Next year, their ages will add up to 50. How old is John? *[64% got this right.]*

13. Here is a quadratic equation: $3x^2 + 17x - 28.9207 = 0$. One of the following is a solution. Which one? *[39% got this right.]*

    (i) 0.87   (ii) 1.37   (iii) 2.17   (iv) 3.81

14. The graph of a straight line is shown below. The line has the equation

$$y = \frac{1}{3}x + 2.$$

Does the point $(5.1, 3.6)$ lie on the line, or can this be determined from the information given? *[49% got this right.]*

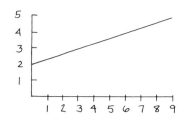

15. Someone is going to drive at a constant speed from San Francisco to Los Angeles by way of Palo Alto. The driver is wondering what speed to choose. Here are four factors of interest:

    I   the distance from San Francisco after 1 hour
    II   the time required to go 100 miles
    III   the distance to Palo Alto after 1 hour
    IV   the distance to LA after 1 hour

Distance is measured along the highway. Six graphs are shown at the top of the next page. Each point on a graph represents a whole trip, the constant speed of the car being shown along the horizontal axis. In four of the graphs, one of the factors listed above is plotted along the vertical axis.

Match the graph with the factor. *[6% got this right.]*

    I   a   b   c   d   e   f
    II   a   b   c   d   e   f
    III   a   b   c   d   e   f
    IV   a   b   c   d   e   f

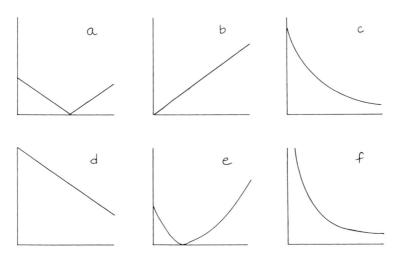

Probability

16. One of the two boxes below will be shaken, and a marble will be drawn out at random. If it is red you will win $1.

    Box A | 9 red marbles   Box B | 90 red marbles
          | 1 blue marble | 10 blue marbles

    (i)   Box A is better.   *[8% chose this option.]*
    (ii) Box B is better.   *[7% chose this option.]*
    (iii) Both boxes offer the same chance of winning.   *[80% chose this option.]*

17. You throw one die. What is the chance of getting an ace ⚀?   *[83% got this right.]*

18. You throw a pair of dice. What is the chance of getting two aces ⚀⚀? *[48% got this right.]*

19. A coin will be tossed either 2 times or 100 times. You will win $2 if the number of heads is equal to the number of tails, no more and no less.

    (i)   2 tosses is better.   *[28% chose this option.]*
    (ii) 100 tosses is better.   *[21% chose this option.]*
    (iii) Both offer the same chance of winning.   *[45% chose this option.]*

20. Here are two situations·

    A) A coin will be tossed 100 times. If it comes up heads 60 or more times you win $1.
    B) A coin will be tossed 1,000 times. If it comes up heads 600 or more times you will win $1.
       (i) Situation A is better.   *[21% chose this option]*
       (ii) Situation B is better.   *[9% chose this option.]*

      (iii) Both offer the same chance of winning. *[64% chose this option.]*

[The percents in 16, 19, 20 do not add to 100%, because about 5% of the students did not choose any option.]

Calculus

Have you had a college calculus course?   Yes <u>37%</u>   No <u>63%</u>

If yes, please work this section.

21. Differentiate x^3. *[83% got this right.]*

22. Find $\int_{-1}^{2} x^3\, dx$. *[28% got this right.]*

23. Solve $\dfrac{dy}{dx} = x$. *[21% got this right.]*

24. To find the c which minimizes $(x_1 - c)^2 + (x_2 - c)^2 + (x_3 - c)^2$:
    (i)   Differentiate with respect to x.
    (ii)   Differentiate with respect to c.
    (iii) Can't do it by calculus.

    [22% chose option (i), 19% chose option (ii), 15% chose option (iii), and 44% declined to choose.]

In this section, percents are based on the 117 students who said they had a college calculus course.

The average score on questions 1 through 20 was 10, with an SD of 4. In Statistics 20 (which has a calculus prerequisite and is aimed at students in quantitative fields), the average score on similar tests was around 13 out of 20, with the same SD of 4.

STATISTICS 2   FREEDMAN-PURVES
FALL 1977   MIDTERM

[This test was given to 311 students.]

PRINT YOUR NAME _____

SIGN YOUR NAME _____

LECTURE TIME: 12-1 OR 1-2?

TA'S NAME _____   LAB TIME _____

To get full credit, you must show work.

x	0.1	0.2	0.3	0.4	0.5	0.6	0.7	0.8	0.9
$\sqrt{x}$	0.32	0.45	0.55	0.63	0.71	0.77	0.84	0.89	0.95

z	0.1	0.2	0.25	0.50	0.75	1.00	1.25	1.60	1.75	2.00	2.25
$A(z)$	8%	16%	20%	38%	55%	68%	79%	90%	92%	95%	98%

1. In a large lecture course, the scores on the final examination followed the normal curve closely. The average score was 60 points and three-fourths of the class scored between 50 and 70 points. The SD of the scores was
    (i)   larger than 10 points
    (ii)   smaller than 10 points
    (iii) impossible to say with information given
    Explain your answer.   (10 points)   *[82% got this right.]*

2. The figure below is a histogram for the blood pressures of subjects in a certain study. The percentage who had blood pressures between 120 mm and 140 mm is exactly equal to the area under _____ between those two values. Fill in the blank with one of the two options: histogram, normal curve.   (10 points)   *[68% got this right.]*

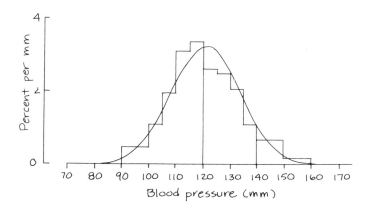

3. Find the correlation coefficient for the data set below.   (20 points)   *[78% got this right.]*

x	y
4	4
4	2
3	1
3	5
1	5
3	7

4. Pearson and Lee obtained the following results for about 1,000 men:

    average height ≈ 69 inches,   SD ≈ 2.5 inches
    average forearm length ≈ 18 inches,   SD ≈ 1 inch, $r ≈ 0.8$

    Of the men who were 6 feet tall (to the nearest inch), about what percentage had forearms shorter than 18 inches?   (20 points)   *[49% got this right.]*

5. In a study of a representative group of men, the correlation between height and weight was 0.43. One man in the study was both one SD above average in height and one SD above average in weight. His weight will be

    (i) larger than   (ii) smaller than   (iii) equal to

    the average weight of all men of his height in the study. Explain your choice. (20 points)   *[61% got this right.]*

6. The figure below is a histogram for the scores on the final in a certain class. Find the 75th percentile of these scores.   (20 points)   *[61% got this right.]*

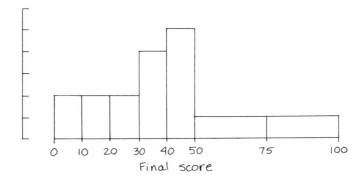

Final score

FINAL IN PSYCHOLOGY 60, STANFORD UNIVERSITY, FALL 1977

This course was taught by Professor J. Merrill Carlsmith, Stanford University, using a trial edition of our book. The final is reproduced with his permission. Some questions are on material covered in lectures not the book. The exam was taken by about 150 students: the median score was 78 out of 100.

Each question is worth 10 points.

1. 60% of the pupils in a particular university are male. What is the probability that a random sample of 400 pupils will contain fewer than 220 males?

2. A random sample of 6 Stanford faculty members gave the following data for number of publications and salary.

Faculty member	Number of Publications	Salary (in 000's)
A	16	20
B	16	25
C	20	22
D	20	30
E	24	28
F	24	25

    (i)   Write the equation of the regression line.

    (ii) If we found another faculty member whose number of publications was 22, what would we guess his salary to be?

    (iii) If in a burst of excitement upon seeing these data, I quickly published 5 more papers, how much would you expect my salary to go up?

    (iv) How would you interpret the intercept of the regression line?

3. I propose to you a new game. You roll 2 dice. If the sum of the numbers showing is either 6, or 7, or 8, I win. If it is 2, 3, 4, 5, 9, 10, 11, 12, you win. Since you have lots more possible winning combinations than I do, the rules are that you pay me $2.00 when I win and I pay you $1.00 when you win. If we play this game 30 times, how much do you think you will win or lose? (I will be in my office this afternoon for anyone who feels like playing.)

4. In an experiment to test the efficacy of Vitamin C in preventing colds, 9 experimental subjects take Vitamin C every day for 1 year, while 4 control subjects take no Vitamin C. The number of colds are tabulated at the end of the year. The thing we are interested in is the size of the reduction in the number of colds which can be attributed to Vitamin C.

    (i) Give an interval which we can be 95% sure covers the true reduction.

    (ii) Does Tukey's quick and dirty test suggest that Vitamin C had an effect?

Experimentals		Controls
0	3	2
0	0	6
1	1	2
2	1	2
1		

5.   A certain town has 25,000 families. The average number of children per family is 2.6, with an SD of 0.80. The distribution is not normal, however, since 25% of the families have no children at all. If we draw a random sample of 90 families, what are the chances that between 23% and 27% of the sample families will have no children?

6.   Last year, baseball instituted what was called the "free agent draft." In essence, this gave players the right to negotiate a contract with any team they chose to, rather than belonging to a particular team forever or until traded. A few of the wealthiest clubs (like the Yankees) promptly paid enormous sums to obtain a few players who had had very high batting averages the previous year. During the course the year, sports writers had lots of fun pointing out what bad judgement the owners had shown, for almost none of these high-priced players did as well this year as they had done the year before. Do you think all that money made the players fat and lazy? Or do you have another explanation?

7.   A large number of measurements on a standard kilogram have established that our weighing procedure gives an average which is 500 micrograms too high, with an SD of 10 micrograms. We have just been sent a new checkweight which we have been asked to weigh. The owners of this checkweight specify that they wish the weight we report to be accurate to within 1 micrograms. We reply that we can't guarantee that, but that we are prepared to guarantee that our answer will be accurate to within 1 micrograms 95% of the time. How many measurements do we need to take?

8.   It is known that nationally, 10% of all lawyers are female. A random sample of lawyers in a particular state yielded 400 males and 100 females. 80% of the sampled male lawyers favored passage of the Equal Rights Amendment, while 90% of the sampled female lawyers favored its passage. Is the difference between male and female lawyers in this state real, or is it just chance variation?

9.   First-born children are less likely to become alcoholic than are later-born children. I wonder whether this fact is also true of birth order with pairs of twins. To study this, I find 8 pairs of twins, and classify each twin as either first-born or second-born. The measure I use is the average daily ingestion of alcohol. Formulate an appropriate null hypothesis and do a test of significance.

| | Twin Pair Number | ALCOHOL INGESTED (ounces) | |
		1st born	2nd born
	1	4	5
	2	0	3
Twin	3	2	2
Pair	4	0	1
Number	5	5	4
	6	3	5
	7	4	5
	8	1	2

10. A study of 500 babies looked at the relationship between their weight at birth and the age at which they first slept through the night. The birth weights averaged out to 90 oz. with an SD of 15 oz. The ages at which they first slept all night averaged 50 days with an SD of 10 days. The correlation between the two variables was −0.60. If we draw a sample of 16 babies who weighed 105 oz. at birth, what is the probability that the average age at which these 16 babies sleep through the night is less than 40? (Hint: You have never seen a problem like this one before, although you have seen all of the component parts.)

**   (For thinking about over the holidays only). You are taking a plane trip and have heard that the odds against someone bringing a bomb on board are 1000 to 1. You are little worried, but then you read that the odds against two people (independently) bringing a bomb on the same plane are 1,000,000 to 1. What should you do? (Bring a bomb on board?)

STATISTICS 2   FREEDMAN-PURVES
FALL 1977   FINAL

[This three-hour test was taken by 294 students.]

Print your name _____

Sign your name _____

Lab time _____

Your TA's name _____

Your instructor's name _____

To get full credit, you must show work. No work, no credit. There is only one exception: problem #5.

square root table		normal table	
x	$\sqrt{x}$	z	$A(z)$
0.10	0.32	0.05	4%
0.15	0.39	0.075	6%
0.20	0.45	0.10	8%
0.22	0.47	0.125	10%
0.25	0.50	0.20	16%
0.30	0.55	0.25	20%
0.35	0.59	0.50	38%
0.40	0.63	0.75	55%
2.70	1.64	1.00	68%
2.80	1.67	1.25	79%
2.90	1.70	1.50	87%
18.00	4.24	2.00	95%
25.00	5.00	2.50	99%

1. Commute Distance (4 points)   *[55% got this right.]*

    As part of a survey, one large manufacturing company asked a thousand of its employees how far they had to commute to work each day (round trip). The data was analyzed by computer and on the printout the average round trip commute distance was reported as 11.3 miles, with an SD of 16.2 miles. Would a rough sketch of the histogram for the data look like (i) or (ii) or (iii)? Or is there a mistake somewhere? Explain your answer.

2. Children's Heights (4 points)   *[46% got this right.]*

A large sample of children was followed over time. One investigator looked at all the children who were at the 90th percentile in height at age four. Some of these children turned out to be above the 90th percentile in height at age eighteen, and others were below. The number who were above was

  (i)   quite a bit smaller than
  (ii) about the same as
  (iii) quite a bit larger than

the number who were below. Or is more information needed? Give a reason to support your answer. (You may assume that the scatter diagram is football-shaped.)

3. The Box (8 points)   *[57% got this right.]*

A hundred draws are made at random with replacement from the box

$$\boxed{0}\ \boxed{0}\ \boxed{0}\ \boxed{1}\ \boxed{2}.$$

Estimate the chance that $\boxed{1}$ turns up on exactly 20 draws. Show your work.

4. Survey Research (4 points)   *[67% got this right.]*

A survey research center conducts frequent opinion polls, using large samples drawn by probability methods which are practically free from bias. Each of the last 100 polls was carried out to estimate a percentage. All the standard errors were computed by the appropriate technique, and turned out to be very close to 3 percentage points. About how many of the estimates were off by more than 3 percentage points? Explain briefly.

5. Blanks (4 points)   *[77% got this right.]*

Fill in the blanks, using one word from each pair below, to make up two true sentences. Write both sentence down.

  If two things are ___(i)___ , and you want to find the chance that ___(ii)___ will happen, you can ___(iii)___ the chances.

  (i)   incompatible, independent
  (ii) both, at least one
  (iii) add, multiply

(In this problem, no work need be shown.)

6. The Speed of Light (8 points)   *[65% got this right.]*

The speed of light is measured 25 times by a new procedure. The 25 measurements are recorded, and show no trend or pattern. Then the investigators work out the average and SD of the 25 numbers; the average is 299,789.2 kilometers per second and the SD is 12 kilometers per second.

(a) Find an approximate 95% confidence interval for the speed of light, showing your work. (You may assume the Gauss model, with no bias.)

(b) Now the investigators measure the speed of light a 26th time by the same procedure, and get 299,781 kilometers per second. Is this a surprising result?

Yes _____   No _____

Check one, and give your reason.

7. Southern California (4 points)   *[39% got this right.]*

Los Angeles has about four times as many registered voters as San Diego. A simple random sample of registered voters is taken in each city, to estimate the percentage who will vote for school bonds. Other things being equal, a sample of 4,000 taken in Los Angeles will be about

(i)   four times as accurate

(ii) twice as accurate

(iii) as accurate

as a sample of 1,000 taken in San Diego. Choose one option and say why.

8. Hospitals (4 points)   *[67% got this right.]*

One hospital has 218 live births during the month of January. Another has 536. Which is likelier to have 55% or more male births? Or is it equally likely? Explain. (There is about a 52% chance for a live-born infant to be male.)

9. The Surveyor (8 points)   *[56% got this right.]*

A surveyor is measuring the distance between five points A, B, C, D, E. They are all on a straight line. He finds that each of the four distances AB, BC, CD, and DE measures one mile, give or take an inch or so. These four measurements are made independently, by the same procedure.

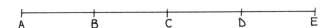

The distance from A to E is about four miles, give or take around

4 inches   2 inches   1 inch   1/2 inch   1/4 inch

Explain briefly. (You may assume the Gauss model, with no bias.)

10. Television (8 points)   *[64% got this right.]*

In a certain town, there are 25,000 households. On the average, there are 1.2 color TV sets per household, with an SD of 0.6; but 10% of the households do not have color TV. As part of a market survey, a simple random sample of 900 households is drawn from the 25,000. What is the chance (approximately) that somewhere between 9% and 11% of the sample households will not have color TV? Show your work.

11. Carnegie (12 points)   *[62% got this right.]*

There are about 2,700 institutions of higher learning in the United States (including junior colleges and community colleges). In 1976, as part of a continuing study of higher education, the Carnegie Commission took a simple random sample of these institutions. The average enrollment in the 225 sample schools was 3,700, with an SD of 6,000. A histogram for the enrollments was plotted and did not follow the normal curve. However, the average enrollment at all 2,700 institutions was estimated to be around 3,700, give or take 400 or so. Say whether each of the following statements is true or false, and explain why.

(a) It is estimated that 95% of the institutions of higher learning in the United States enroll between $3,700 - 800 = 2,900$ and $3,700 + 800 = 4,500$ students.

(b) An approximate 95%-confidence interval for the average enrollment of all 2,700 institutions runs from 2,900 to 4,500.

(c) If someone takes a simple random sample of 225 institutions of higher learning, and goes two SEs either way from the average enrollment of the 225 sample schools, there is about a 95% chance that this interval will cover the average enrollment of all 2,700 schools.

(d) The normal curve can't be used to figure confidence levels here at all, because the data doesn't follow the normal curve.

12. High Schools (8 points)   *[62% got this right.]*

There are about 25,000 high schools in the United States; each high school has a principal. As part of a national survey of education, a simple random sample of 225 high schools is chosen. In 202 of the sample high schools the principal has an advanced degree.

(a) If possible, find an approximate 95% confidence interval for the percentage of all 25,000 high school principals who have advanced degrees, showing your work. If this is impossible, explain why.

The 25,000 high schools in the United States employ a total of about one million teachers. As it turned out, the 225 sample high schools employed a total of 10,000 teachers, of whom 5,010 had advanced degrees.

(b) If possible, find and approximate 95% confidence interval for the percentage of all one million high school teachers with advanced degrees, showing your work. If this is impossible, explain why.

13. Reading (8 points)   *[53% got this right.]*

The National Assessment of Educational Progress (NAEP) administered a reading test to a nationwide probability sample of 9-year-olds in 1971. The same test was administered to an independently chosen sample of 9-year-olds in 1975. There appears to have been some improvement: in 1971, the average score was 67.2 out of 100, while in 1975 the average score was 68.5 out of 100. Or can this be explained as a chance variation? Explain your reasoning.

You may assume the NAEP took independent simple random samples in 1971 and 1975; there were 1,600 children in each sample, and in both years the SD of the scores was very nearly 14 points out of 100.

14. Belmont and Marolla (8 points)   *[34% got this right.]*

Belmont and Marolla conducted a study on the relationship between birth order, family size, and intelligence. The subjects consisted of all Dutch men who reached the age of 19 between 1963 and 1966. These men were required by law to take the Dutch army induction tests, including Raven's intelligence test. The results showed that for each family size, measured intelligence decreased with birth order: first-borns did better than second-borns, second-borns did better than third-borns, and so on. And for any particular birth order, intelligence decreased with family size: for instance, first-borns in two-child families did better than first-borns in three-child families. These results remained true even after controlling for the social class of the parents. Taking, for instance, men from two-child families:

- the first-borns averaged 2.575 on the test;
- the second-borns averaged 2.678 on the test.

(Raven test scores range from 1 to 6, with 1 being best and 6 worst.) The difference is small, but if it is real, it has interesting implications for genetic theory. To show that the difference was real, Belmont and Marolla made a two-sample z-test. The SD for the test scores was around one point, both for the first-borns and the second-borns, and there were 30,000 of each, so

$$\text{SE for sum} \approx \sqrt{30,000} \times 1 \text{ point} \approx 173 \text{ points}$$
$$\text{SE for average} \approx 173/30,000 \approx 0.006 \text{ points}$$
$$\text{SE for difference} \approx \sqrt{(0.006)^2 + (0.006)^2} \approx 0.008 \text{ points.}$$

Therefore, $z = (2.575 - 2.678)/0.008 \approx -12.6$, and P is astonishingly small. Belmont and Marolla concluded:

> Thus the observed difference was highly significant...a high level of statistical confidence can be placed in each average because of the large number of cases.

Was it appropriate to make a two-sample z-test in this situation?

Yes _____   No _____

Check one, and justify it.

15. The Effects of Exercise (8 points)   *[59% got this right.]*

An investigator in the Statistics Department of a large university is interested in the effect of exercise in maintaining mental ability. He decides to study the faculty members aged 40 to 50 at his university, looking separately at two groups: The ones that exercise regularly, and the ones that don't. There turn out to be several hundred people in each group, so he takes simple random sample of 25 persons from each group, for detailed study. One of the things he does is to administer an IQ test to the sample people, with the following results:

	Regular exercise	No regular exercise
Sample size	25	25
Average score	135	121
SD of scores	15	15

The difference between the averages is "highly statistically significant." The investigator concludes that exercise does indeed help to maintain mental ability among the faculty members aged 40 to 50 at his university. Is this conclusion justified?

                        Yes _____   No _____

Check one, and say why.

Test Results from the Second Edition

STATISTICS 2/20   FREEDMAN-PURVES
FALL 1988   DIAGNOSTIC QUIZ

This quiz was taken by 23 students in Statistics 20 and 251 students in Statistics 2. A very similar quiz was taken by 316 students in Statistics 2, Fall 1977: see pp. 103–105. (Statistics 20 has a calculus prerequisite and is taught in small sections.) Results are tabulated for all three courses: the "pass rate" is the percentage of students giving the right answer.

This is a diagnostic quiz to help us determine the general level of mathematical ability in the class. Many of the skills tested in the quiz will not be used in the course. Your score on this quiz will not affect your grade, but please do your best. If you do not know the answer to a question, do not guess—just leave it blank.

1. 300 is what percent of 2,000?

	Pass Rate
Statistics 20, Fall 1988	*87%*
Statistics 2, Fall 1977	*74%*
Statistics 2, Fall 1988	*74%*

2. A town has 100,000 families; 0.1 of 1% of these families have incomes over $75,000 a year. The number of such families is _____.

	Pass Rate
Statistics 20, Fall 1988	*83%*
Statistics 2, Fall 1977	*71%*
Statistics 2, Fall 1988	*63%*

3. There are 100 million eligible voters in the United States. The Gallup poll interviews 5,000 of them. This amounts to 1 eligible voter out of every _____.

	Pass Rate
Statistics 20, Fall 1988	*65%*
Statistics 2, Fall 1977	*61%*
Statistics 2, Fall 1988	*51%*

4. In the United States, 1 person out of every 200 is in the army, and 8 out of every 10,000 are army officers. What percentage of army personnel are officers, or can this be determined from the information given?

	Pass Rate
Statistics 20, Fall 1988	*30%*
Statistics 2, Fall 1977	*20%*
Statistics 2, Fall 1988	*15%*

5. In the United States, 1 person out of every 500 is in the navy, and one-sixth of naval personnel are officers. What fraction of the US population consists of naval officers? Or can this be determined from the information given?

	Pass Rate
Statistics 20, Fall 1988	*52%*
Statistics 2, Fall 1977	*27%*
Statistics 2, Fall 1988	*27%*

6. $\sqrt{100,000}$ is about:

    (a) 30   (b) 300   (c) 1,000   (d) 3,000   (e) Can't tell

	Pass Rate
Statistics 20, Fall 1988	*74%*
Statistics 2, Fall 1977	*64%*
Statistics 2, Fall 1988	*57%*

7. $\sqrt{17}/17 = 17/\sqrt{17}$

    (a) True   (b) False   (c) Don't know

	Pass Rate
Statistics 20, Fall 1988	*96%*
Statistics 2, Fall 1977	*81%*
Statistics 2, Fall 1988	*82%*

8. $\sqrt{0.5}$ is smaller than 0.5

    (a) True   (b) False   (c) Don't know

	Pass Rate
Statistics 20, Fall 1988	*44%*
Statistics 2, Fall 1977	*41%*
Statistics 2, Fall 1988	*36%*

9. $\sqrt{2.5^2 + 3.4^2} = 2.5 + 3.4$

    (a) True   (b) False   (c) Don't know

	Pass Rate
Statistics 20, Fall 1988	*74%*
Statistics 2, Fall 1977	*59%*
Statistics 2, Fall 1988	*47%*

10. A quart of vodka is 40% alcohol. Write a formula for the percentage of alcohol in a mixture of V quarts of vodka and J quarts of orange juice.

	Pass Rate
Statistics 20, Fall 1988	48%
Statistics 2, Fall 1977	15%
Statistics 2, Fall 1988	8%

11.   This year John's mother is exactly three times as old as he is. Next year, their ages will add up to 50. How old is John?

	Pass Rate
Statistics 20, Fall 1988	87%
Statistics 2, Fall 1977	64%
Statistics 2, Fall 1988	69%

12.   Here is a quadratic equation: $3x^2 + 17x - 28.9207 = 0$. One of the following is a solution; which one?

(a) 0.87   (b) 1.37   (c) 2.17   (d) 3.81

	Pass Rate
Statistics 20, Fall 1988	74%
Statistics 2, Fall 1977	39%
Statistics 2, Fall 1988	39%

13.   The graph of a straight line is shown below. The line has the equation $y = 0.33x + 2$. Does the point $(5.1, 3.6)$ lie on the line? Or can this be determined from the information given?

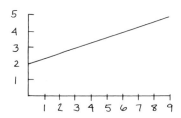

	Pass Rate
Statistics 20, Fall 1988	74%
Statistics 2, Fall 1977	49%
Statistics 2, Fall 1988	61%

14.   You throw one die. What is the chance of getting an ace ⚀ ?

	Pass Rate
Statistics 20, Fall 1988	96%
Statistics 2, Fall 1977	83%
Statistics 2, Fall 1988	88%

15.   You throw a pair of dice. What is the chance of getting two aces ⚀⚀ ?

	Pass Rate
Statistics 20, Fall 1988	*78%*
Statistics 2, Fall 1977	*48%*
Statistics 2, Fall 1988	*41%*

16. Here are two situations:

    (i) A coin will be tossed 100 times. If it comes up heads 60 or more times, you win $1.

    (ii) A coin will be tossed 1,000 times. If it comes up heads 600 or more times, you win $1.

    Which is better? Or do they offer the same chance of winning?

	Pass Rate
Statistics 20, Fall 1988	*22%*
Statistics 2, Fall 1977	*21%*
Statistics 2, Fall 1988	*14%*

The denominators for pass rates in question 17–20 include all students in the class, whether or not they have had a college calculus course.

17. Differentiate x^2.

	Pass Rate
Statistics 20, Fall 1988	*83%*
Statistics 2, Fall 1988	*29%*

18. Find $\int_{-1}^{2} x^2 \, dx$.

	Pass Rate
Statistics 20, Fall 1988	*52%*
Statistics 2, Fall 1988	*14%*

19. Solve $\dfrac{dy}{dx} = x$.

	Pass Rate
Statistics 20, Fall 1988	*43%*
Statistics 2, Fall 1988	*10%*

20. To find the c which minimizes $(x_1 - c)^2 + (x_2 - c)^2 + (x_3 - c)^2$:

    (a) Differentiate with respect to x.

    (b) Differentiate with respect to c.

    (c) Can't do it by calculus.

	Pass Rate
Statistics 20, Fall 1988	*65%*
Statistics 2, Fall 1988	*9%*

STATISTICS 20   MR. FREEDMAN
FALL 1989   MIDTERM

[37 students took this test]

1. According to an observational study done at Kaiser Permanente in Walnut
    Creek, California, users of oral contraceptives have a higher rate of cervical
    cancer than non-users, even after adjusting for age, education, marital status,
    religion, and smoking. Investigators concluded that the pill causes cervical can-
    cer. Were they right to do so? Answer yes or no, and explain briefly.   *[84% got
    this right.]*

2. The sketches show results of two studies on the pill, for women age 25–29. In
    one study, the pill adds about 10 mm to blood pressures; in the other, the pill
    adds about 10%. Which is which, and why?   *[95% got this right.]*

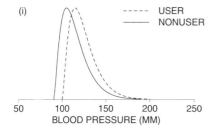 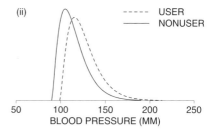

3. In 1983, investigators administered questionnaires to Russian emigres in New
    York. Subjects who described KGB leaders as "competent" also said they par-
    ticipated less often in political protests in Russia. The correlation remained
    after adjusting for age, education, and status. The investigators concluded:

    > ... persons who perceived the KGB to be highly competent were less
    > likely to engage in unorthodox behavior ... perceptions of the KGB's com-
    > petence serve to deter would-be nonconformists.

    Is the conclusion justified? Answer yes or no, and explain briefly.   *[32% got
    this right.]*

4. The great French kings of history had mediocre chief ministers, while the great
    ministers served under kings of lesser talent. Is this a fact of French history? or
    of statistics? Discuss briefly.   *[43% got this right.]*

5. The figure at the top of the next page is a scatter plot of income against edu-
    cation, for a representative sample of men age 25–29 in Texas in 1988. Or is
    something wrong? Explain briefly.   *[46% got this right.]*

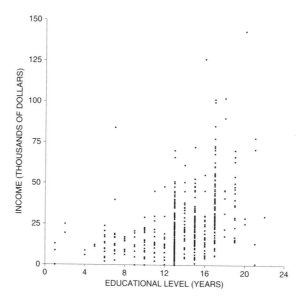

6. For women age 25–29 in California, the relationship between income and education can be summarized as follows.

$$\text{average education} = 12 \text{ years}, \quad \text{SD} = 3.5 \text{ years}$$
$$\text{average income} = \$11{,}600, \quad \text{SD} = \$10{,}500, \quad r = 0.4$$

(The scatter diagram has the same general shape as the one in problem 5 above.)
   (a) Find the r.m.s. error of the regression line for predicting income from education.
   (b) Predict the income of a woman with 14 years of education.
   (c) This prediction is likely to be off by $_____ or so. Or can this be determined from the information given?
   (d) Repeat parts (b) and (c), for a woman with 10 years of education.
   [89% got at least half credit on this question]

7. A coin will be tossed 10 times. Find the chance that there will be 2 heads among the first 5 tosses, and 4 heads among the last 5 tosses.   *[73% got this right.]*

STATISTICS 20   Mr. FREEDMAN
FALL 1989   FINAL

[35 students took this three-hour test]

1. DES was given to pregnant women to prevent miscarriage. A literature review found 3 randomized controlled experiments, and 5 nonrandomized studies with control groups. The rate of miscarriages was about the same in the treatment groups, for all 8 studies. The rate was also about the same in the 3 control groups, for the randomized controlled experiments. However, the rate was substantially higher among the control groups in the 5 nonrandomized studies. How do you interpret these data?   *[71% got this right.]*

2. By Census definitions, a "family" consists of 2 or more related persons living together; a "household" has 1 or more people living in the same housing unit. In 1987, the average income for households was about 10% less than the average income for families. How can this be? Discuss briefly.   *[86% got this right.]*

3. A statistical analysis is made of the midterm and final scores in a large course, with the following results:

    $$\text{average midterm score} \approx 60, \quad SD \approx 15$$
    $$\text{average final score} \approx 65, \quad SD \approx 20, \quad r \approx 0.50$$

    The scatter diagram is football-shaped.
    (a) About what percentage of students scored over 80 on the final?
    (b) Of the students who scored 80 on the midterm, about what percentage scored over 80 on the final?

    [91% got at least half credit for this question.]

4. The unconditional probability of event A is $1/3$; the unconditional probability of B is $1/10$. True or false, and explain:
    (a) If A and B are independent, they must also be mutually exclusive.
    (b) If A and B are mutually exclusive, they cannot be independent.

    [69% got at least half credit for this question.]

5. A gambler plays roulette 100 times. There are two possibilities:
    (A) Betting $1 on a section each time.
    (B) Betting $1 on red each time.
    A section bet pays 2 to 1, and there are 12 chances in 38 to win. Red pays even money, and there are 18 chances in 38 to win. True or false, and explain:
    (a) The chance of coming out ahead is the same with A and B.
    (b) The chance of winning more than $10 is bigger with A.
    (c) The chance of losing more than $10 is bigger with A.

    [80% got at least half credit for this question.]

6. Shown below are probability histograms for the sum of 100, 400 and 900 draws from the box

    $$\boxed{99 \,\boxed{0}\text{'s} \quad \boxed{1}}.$$

    Which histogram is which? Why?   *[97% got this right.]*

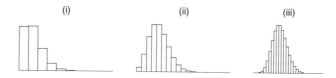

7. On Sunday, September 11, 1988, the *San Francisco Examiner* ran a story headlined—

    ### 3 IN 10 BIOLOGY TEACHERS BACK BIBLICAL CREATIONISM

    Arlington, Texas. Thirty percent of high school biology teachers polled believe in the biblical creation and 19 percent incorrectly think that humans and dinosaurs lived at the same time, according to a nationwide survey published Saturday.

    "We're doing something very, very, very wrong in biology education," said Dana Dunn, one of two sociologists at the University of Texas, Arlington.

    Dunn and Raymond Eve sent questionnaires to 20,000 high school biology teachers selected at random from a list provided by the National Science Teachers Association and received 200 responses....

    In fact, the investigators chose 400 teachers at random from the National Science Teachers Association list, sent questionnaires to these 400 teachers, and received 200 replies. Why do these details matter?   *[97% got this right; however, the question has been edited, see note 25 to the chapter, so the pass rate may not be directly applicable.]*

8. One hospital has 218 live births during the month of January. Another has 536. Which is likelier to have 55% or more male births? Or is it equally likely? Explain. (There is about a 52% chance for a live-born infant to be male.)   *[91% got this right.]*

9. A survey organization takes a simple random sample of 625 households from a city of 80,000 households. On the average, there are 2.30 persons per sample household, and the SD is 1.75. Say whether each of the following statements is true or false, and explain.   *[77% got at least half credit for this question.]*

    (a) The 2.30 is 0.07 or so off the average number of persons per household in the whole city.

    (b) A 95%-confidence interval for the average household size in the sample is 2.16 to 2.44.

(c) A 95%-confidence interval for the average household size in the city is 2.16 to 2.44.

(d) 95% of the households in the city contain between 2.16 and 2.44 persons.

(e) Household size in the city follows the normal curve.

(f) The 95%-confidence level is about right because household size follows the normal curve.

10. A machine makes sticks of butter whose average weight is 4.0 ounces; the SD of the weights is 0.05 ounces. There is no trend or pattern in the data. There are 4 sticks to a package.   *[91% got at least half credit for this question.]*

   (a) A package weighs _____ give or take _____ or so.

   (b) A store buys 100 packages. Estimate the chance that they get 100 pounds of butter, to within 2 ounces.

11. As part of a statistics project, Mr. Frank Alpert approached the first 100 students he saw one day on Sproul Plaza at the University of California, Berkeley, and found out the school or college in which they enrolled. His sample included 53 men and 47 women. From Registrar's data, 25,000 students were registered at Berkeley that term, and 67% were male. Was his sampling procedure like taking a simple random sample?   *[23% got this right.]*

12. A geography test was given to a simple random sample of 250 high school students in a certain large school district. One question involved an outline map of Europe, with the countries identified only by number. The students were asked to pick out Great Britain and France. As it turned out, 65.8% could find France, compared to 70.2% for Great Britain. Is the difference statistically significant? Or can this be determined from the information given?   *[29% got this right.]*

13. One study of grand juries in Alameda County, California, compared the demographic characteristics of jurors with the general population, to see if the jury panels were representative. Here are the results for age. (Only persons 21 and over are considered; the county age distribution is known from Public Health Department data.)

Age	County-wide percentage	Number of jurors
21 to 40	42	5
41 to 50	23	9
51 to 60	16	19
61 and up	19	33
Total	100	66

Were these 66 jurors selected at random from the population of Alameda County (age 21 and up)?   *[63% got this right.]*

14. R.E. Just and W.S. Chern claimed that the buyers of California canning toma-
     toes exercised market power to fix prices. As proof, the investigators estimated
     the price elasticity of demand for tomatoes in two periods—before and after the
     introduction of mechanical harvesters. (An elasticity of −5, for instance, means
     that a 1% increase in prices causes a 5% drop in demand.) They put standard
     errors on the estimates.

     In a competitive market, the harvester should make no difference in demand
     elasticity; it only affects supply. However, the difference between the two es-
     timated elasticities—pre-harvester and post-harvester—was statistically signif-
     icant ($z \approx 1.56$, $P \approx 5.9\%$, one-sided). The investigators tried several ways
     of estimating the price elasticity before settling on the final version. Comment
     briefly on the use of statistical tests. *[69% got this right.]*

STATISTICS 2   Mr. PURVES
FALL 1990   FINAL EXAM

Print your name _____

Sign your name _____

TA's name _____

Section time _____

To get full credit, you must give reasons and/or show work.

This three-hour test was taken by 209 students. The average score was 56/100, and the SD was 22.

1. Here is a passage from Dr. Dean Edell's column in the San Francisco Chronicle of August 1, 1990.

    ### DEMAND AN EXPERIENCED SURGEON

    The more experienced a doctor is, the better. As obvious as that sounds, there are still too many people out there who never ask their surgeons for a history of their work. The importance of knowing is illustrated by this study.

    Peter Starek, a surgeon at the University of North Carolina, reviewed 460 heart valve replacement operations and found that only 4 percent of the patients of the three most senior surgeons died. But one junior surgeon lost almost a third of his patients. Since that surgeon was technically the best in the group, says Starek, something was obviously lacking—perhaps the kind of good judgment that grows out of experience ...

    The last sentence of the paragraph contains the claim that the junior surgeon was obviously lacking something—"perhaps the kind of good judgment that grows out of experience." Is the claim justified by Dr. Starek's evidence? Discuss briefly.

2. According to an article in the November 28, 1990 edition of the San Francisco Chronicle, 74 percent of the freshman class at UC Berkeley scored over 500 points on the verbal section of the SAT. If the verbal SAT scores for the entire class have an SD of 80 points and follow the normal curve, what is the average?

3. For the 988 men age 18–24 in the HANES sample,

    $$\text{average height} \approx 70 \text{ inches,} \qquad \text{SD} \approx 3 \text{ inches}$$
    $$\text{average weight} \approx 162 \text{ pounds,} \qquad \text{SD} \approx 30 \text{ pounds}$$
    $$\text{correlation} \approx 0.47$$

    One man in the sample was 66 inches tall and weighed 140 pounds. In comparison with the other men in the sample of the same height, this man would be

a little light   a little heavy.

Circle one option and explain your choice.

4. A computer printout shows the following descriptive statistics on the relationship between blood pressure and height for a large representative sample of American men:

average height $\approx$ 70 inches,   average blood pressure $\approx$ 124 mm
correlation between height and blood pressure $\approx$ −0.2

It also shows the regression equation for predicting blood pressure from height:

predicted blood pressure $=$ (−0.9 mm per inch) $\times$ height $+$ 163 mm

Is there anything wrong? To answer, choose one option below and then explain your choice.

(a) There may be something wrong, but there is not enough information here to decide.

(b) Something is definitely wrong.

5. Two draws are made at random with replacement from the box

| Z | E | B | R | A |

(a) What is the chance that the letters are different?

(b) What is the chance of getting a vowel at least once in the two draws?

6. A box of tickets averages out to 75, and the SD is 10. Twenty-five draws are made at random with replacement from this box.

(a) Find the chance (approximately) that the average of the draws will be in the range 65 to 85.

(b) Repeat, for the range 74 to 76.

7. A sociologist draws a simple random sample of 500 students from the undergraduates at a large state university. The students are interviewed about their plans upon graduation, and their responses recorded on interview forms. The names of the students, along with the responses, are entered in a computer file in the same order as they were originally chosen for the sample. Unfortunately, before anyone could look at the results, a programming error led to the loss of data for the last 100 students in the file. Eventually, the lost data will be reentered into the computer from the interview forms, but the sociologist wants to start working on the available data immediately. For example, he finds that out of the 400 students whose responses are still intact, 80 plan to go on to graduate school. Using this 80 out of 400, the sociologist intends to calculate a 95% confidence interval for the percentage of undergraduates at the university

who plan to go to graduate school. Is this appropriate? If it is, explain why and find the confidence interval; if not, explain why not.

(Note: Please choose one and only one of the two options. For example do not write, "I don't think the calculation is appropriate, but in case it is, here is how to find the confidence interval" and then go on to do the calculation of the confidence interval.)

8. A simple random sample of 1,000 persons is taken to estimate the percentage of Democrats in a large population. It turns out that 543 of the people in the sample are Democrats. The sample percentage is $(543/1{,}000) \times 100\% = 54.3\%$. The SE for the sample percentage of Democrats is figured as 1.6%. True or false, and explain:

   (a) $54.3\% \pm 3.2\%$ is a 95%-confidence interval for the percentage of Democrats in the population.

   (b) $54.3\% \pm 3.2\%$ is a 95%-confidence interval for the percentage of Democrats in the sample.

   (c) There are about two chances in three for the percentage of Democrats in the population to be in the range $54.3\% \pm 1.6\%$.

9. The students in a high school physics class made 25 measurements of the weight of a piece of metal about the size of a nickel. On their first weighing, they got 5.29 grams. On their next one, they got 5.36 grams. On their final weighing—the 25th one—they got 5.37 grams. All the results are shown below.

Meas No.	Result	Meas No.	Result	Meas No.	Result	Meas No.	Result	Meas No.	Result
1	5.29	6	5.47	11	5.58	16	5.59	21	5.49
2	5.36	7	5.49	12	5.64	17	5.56	22	5.48
3	5.37	8	5.50	13	5.72	18	5.53	23	5.47
4	5.41	9	5.52	14	5.65	19	5.52	24	5.39
5	5.44	10	5.54	15	5.62	20	5.50	25	5.37

If it is reasonable to do so, find an approximate 95%-confidence interval for the weight of the piece of metal. If it is not reasonable, explain why not. (The 25 numbers in the table have an average of 5.5 grams and an SD of 0.1 grams.)

10. Here is a quotation from the San Francisco Chronicle of June 23, 1990. (The quote has been edited slightly.)

   The same poll contained equal helpings of good news and bad news for Dianne Feinstein's bid to become California's first woman governor. The survey of 1330 registered voters found Democrat Feinstein with a statistically _____ lead over Republican Pete Wilson of 52 percent to 48 percent...

One word has been left out. That word is either:

   significant   or   insignificant

For the questions below, you may assume the survey consisted of a simple random sample of 1330 registered California voters.

(a) Formulate the null hypothesis implicit in the passage. Translate it into a statement about a box model.

(b) Calculate the appropriate test statistic and find the observed significance level.

(c) Was the missing word "significant" or "insignificant?"

11. Freshmen at public universities work 12.2 hours a week for pay, on average, and the SD is 10.5 hours; at private universities, the average is 9.2 hours and the SD is 9.9 hours. Assume these data are based on two independent simple random samples, each of size 1,000. Is the difference between the averages due to chance?

(a) Formulate the null hypothesis as a statement about a box model.

(b) Repeat (a) for alternative hypothesis.

(c) Calculate the appropriate test statistic.

(d) What do you conclude?

Test Results from the Third Edition

This is a diagnostic quiz to help us determine the general level of mathematical ability in the class. Many of the skills tested in the quiz will not be used in the course. Your score on this quiz will not affect your grade, but please do your best. If you do not know the answer to a question, do not guess—just leave it blank.

Statistics 2, Fall, 1995; N = 286.
Statistics 20, Fall, 1995; N = 43.

1. 300 is what percent of 2,000?

   Statistics 2: 71% got this right.
   Statistics 20: 88% got this right.

2. A town has 100,000 families; 0.1 of 1% of these families have incomes over $75,000 a year. The number of such families is _____.

   Statistics 2: 60% got this right.
   Statistics 20: 77% got this right.

3. There are 100 million eligible voters in the United States. The Gallup poll interviews 5,000 of them. This amounts to 1 eligible voter out of every _____.

   Statistics 2: 53% got this right.
   Statistics 20: 72% got this right.

4. In the United States, 1 person out of every 500 is in the army, and 3 out of every 10,000 are army officers. What percentage of army personnel are officers, or can this be determined from the information given?

   Statistics 2: 17% got this right.
   Statistics 20: 37% got this right.

5. In the United States, 1 person out of every 1,500 is a marine, and one-tenth of marine personnel are officers. What fraction of the US population consists of marine officers? Or can this be determined from the information given?

   Statistics 2: 31% got this right.
   Statistics 20: 60% got this right.

6. $\sqrt{100,000}$ is about:

   (a) 30   (b) 300   (c) 1,000   (d) 3,000   (e) Can't tell

Statistics 2: 49% got this right.
Statistics 20: 84% got this right.

7. $\sqrt{17}/17 = 17/\sqrt{17}$

    (a) True   (b) False   (c) Don't know

Statistics 2: 90% got this right.
Statistics 20: 100% got this right.

8. $\sqrt{0.5}$ is smaller than 0.5

    (a) True   (b) False   (c) Don't know

Statistics 2: 33% got this right.
Statistics 20: 67% got this right.

9. $\sqrt{2.5^2 + 3.4^2} = 2.5 + 3.4$

    (a) True   (b) False   (c) Don't know

Statistics 2: 62% got this right.
Statistics 20: 79% got this right.

10. A quart of vodka is 40% alcohol. Write a formula for the percentage of alcohol in a mixture of V quarts of vodka and J quarts of orange juice.

Statistics 2: 13% got this right.
Statistics 20: 16% got this right.

11. This year John's mother is exactly three times as old as he is. Next year, their ages will add up to 50. How old is John?

Statistics 2: 52% got this right.
Statistics 20: 77% got this right.

12. Here is a quadratic equation: $3x^2 + 17x - 28.9207 = 0$. One of the following is a solution; which one?

    (a) 0.87   (b) 1.37   (c) 2.17   (d) 3.81

Statistics 2: 32% got this right.
Statistics 20: 63% got this right.

13. The graph of the equation $y = \frac{1}{3}x + 2$ is a straight line. Does the point $(5.1, 3.5)$ lie on the line?

    (a) Yes _____   (b) No _____

    (c) This can't be determined from the given information _____

Statistics 2: 64% got this right.
Statistics 20: 81% got this right.

14. You throw one die. What is the chance of getting an ace ⚀ ?

Statistics 2: 90% got this right.
Statistics 20: 98% got this right.

15. You throw a pair of dice. What is the chance of getting two aces ⊡⊡?

> *Statistics 2: 48% got this right.*
> *Statistics 20: 74% got this right.*

16. Here are two situations:
    (i) A coin will be tossed 100 times. If it comes up heads 60 or more times, you win $1.
    (ii) A coin will be tossed 1,000 times. If it comes up heads 600 or more times, you win $1.

    Which is better? Or do they offer the same chance of winning?

> *Statistics 2: 19% got this right.*
> *Statistics 20: 28% got this right.*

Have you had a college-level calculus course?   Yes _____   No _____

> *Statistics 20: 100% have had a college level calculus course.*

17. Differentiate x^2.

> *Statistics 2: 47% got this right.*
> *Statistics 20: 95% got this right.*

18. Find $\int_{-1}^{2} x^3 \, dx$.

> *Statistics 2: 19% got this right.*
> *Statistics 20: 60% got this right.*

19. Solve $\dfrac{dy}{dx} = x$.

> *Statistics 2: 13% got this right.*
> *Statistics 20: 23% got this right.*

20. To find the c which minimizes $(x_1 - c)^2 + (x_2 - c)^2 + (x_3 - c)^2$:
    (a) Differentiate with respect to x.
    (b) Differentiate with respect to c.
    (c) Can't do it by calculus.

> *Statistics 2: 13% got this right.*
> *Statistics 20: 26% got this right.*

Means and SDs

Statistics 2: Mean is 9, SD is 4
Statistics 20: Mean is 13, SD is 3

STATISTICS 20   Mr. FREEDMAN
FALL 1995   MIDTERM

This test has 8 questions on 4 pages; there is a normal table on page 4. Question 5 is worth 16 points; the others are worth 12 points each. Please write in ink on the right hand pages of a blue book; scratch work can be done on the left hand pages. Show work; style counts.

NO BOOKS OR NOTES. CALCULATORS OK.

54 students took this test; the mean was 72, and the SD was 18. The "pass rate" for each question is the percent getting half marks or better.

Question 1. *[Pass rate is 85%.]*

California is evaluating a new program to rehabilitate prisoners before their release; the object is to reduce the "recidivism rate"—the percentage who will be back in prison within two years of release. The program involves several months of "boot camp"—military-style basic training with very strict discipline. Admission to the program is voluntary. According to a prison spokesman, "Those who complete boot camp are less likely to return to prison than other inmates."

 (a) What is the treatment group? the control group?

 (b) True or false: the prison spokesman's comparison is based on an observational study. If true, could a randomized controlled experiment be done to evaluate boot camp? Explain briefly.

 (c) True or false: the data show that boot camp worked. Explain briefly.

Question 2. *[Pass rate is 41%.]*

The figure below (adapted from the San Francisco Chronicle, May 18, 1992) shows the distribution of American families by income in 1992. Ranges include the left endpoint but not the right. For example, 3.7% of the families had incomes in the range $0–$4,999, 5.8% had incomes in the range $5,000–$9,999, and so forth. True or false, and explain:

 (a) Although American families are not spread evenly over the whole income range, the families that earn between $10,000 and $35,000 are spread fairly evenly over that range.

 (b) The families that earn between $35,000 and $75,000 are spread fairly evenly over that range.

 (c) The graph is a histogram.

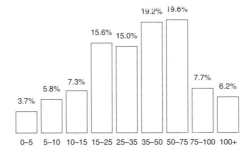

Question 3. *[Pass rate is 77%.]*

Among first-year students at a certain university, scores on the Verbal SAT follow the normal curve; the average is always around 500 and the SD is about 100.

(a) What percentage of these students have scores in range 350 to 650?

(b) One year, there were about 1,000 students with scores in the range 400–600 on the Verbal SAT. About _____ of them had scores in the range 450 to 550. Fill in the blank, using one of the options below; explain briefly. Options: 440, 500, 560.

Question 4. *[Pass rate is 87%.]*

(a) Find the correlation coefficient for the data set in table (i) below.

(b) If possible, fill in the blanks in table (ii) below so the correlation coefficient is 1. If this is not possible, explain why not.

	(i)			(ii)	
x	y		x	y	
4	7		—	7	
5	0		5	—	
7	9		7	9	
8	9		8	9	
8	13		8	13	
10	16		10	—	

Question 5. *[Pass rate is 85%.]*

A statistical analysis was made of the midterm and final scores in a large course, with the following results:

$$\text{average midterm score} = 50, \quad \text{SD} = 25$$
$$\text{average final score} = 55, \quad \text{SD} = 15, \quad r = 0.60$$

The scatter diagram was football-shaped. For each student, the final score was predicted from the midterm score using the regression line.

(a) For about 1/3 of the students, the prediction for the final score was off by more than _____ points. Options: 6, 9, 12, 15, 25

(b) Predict the final score for a student whose midterm score was 80.

(c) This prediction is likely to be off by _____ points or so. Options: 6, 9, 12, 15, 25

(d) Of the students who scored 80 on the midterm, about what percentage scored over 80 on the final?

Question 6. *[Pass rate is 93%.]*

A scatter diagram is shown at the top of the next page, with two lines. One estimates the average value of y for each x. The other estimates the average value of x for each y. Or is something wrong? Explain briefly.

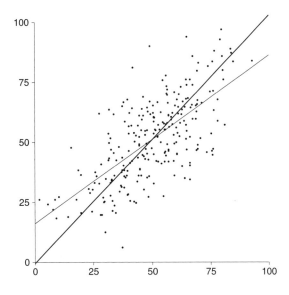

Question 7. *[Pass rate is 87%.]*

The unconditional probability of event A is $1/2$. The unconditional probability of event B is $1/3$. Say whether each of the following is true or false, and explain briefly.

(a) The chance that A and B both happen must be $1/2 \times 1/3 = 1/6$.

(b) If A and B are independent, the chance that they both happen must be $1/2 \times 1/3 = 1/6$.

(c) If A and B are mutually exclusive, the chance that they both happen must be $1/2 \times 1/3 = 1/6$.

(d) The chance that at least one of A or B happens must be $1/2 + 1/3 = 5/6$.

(e) If A and B are independent, the chance that at least one of them happens must be $1/2 + 1/3 = 5/6$.

(f) If A and B are mutually exclusive, the chance that at least one of them happens must be $1/2 + 1/3 = 5/6$.

Question 8. *[Pass rate is 78%.]*

Three cards are dealt from a well shuffled deck.

(a) Find the chance that all of the cards are diamonds.

(b) Find the chance that none of the cards are diamonds.

(c) Find the chance that the cards are not all diamonds.

STATISTICS 20   Mr. FREEDMAN
FALL 1995   FINAL

This test has 14 questions. Each is printed on a separate page. Write your answer on the question sheet or the blank page which follows. A normal table is at the end.

SHOW WORK. STYLE COUNTS.

50 students took the test; the average score was 70, with an SD of 17. The percentage getting half marks or better is shown for each question, as the "pass rate."

Question 1. *[Pass rate is 74%.]*

Smokers have about three times the death rate from cirrhosis as non-smokers, after adjusting for age and sex. However, alcohol consumption is a confounding variable. This means—

(i) Alcohol causes cirrhosis.

(ii) Drinking is associated with smoking, and alcohol causes cirrhosis.

Choose one option and explain briefly.

Question 2. *[Pass rate is 36%.]*

The US Department of Justice made a study of civil jury cases in state courts in the nation's 75 largest counties. In these courts, during the year ending 30 June 1992, juries gave money damages to plaintiffs in 5,949 cases. The median amount was $50,000, and the average was $450,000. Percentiles were computed for this distribution. Which of the following two differences is bigger? Or are they the same? Explain briefly.

(i) 50th percentile − 10th percentile

(ii) 90th percentile − 50th percentile

Question 3. *[Pass rate is 62%.]*

Many observers think there is a permanent underclass in American society—most of those in poverty typically remain poor from year to year. Over the period 1970–90, the percentage of the American population in poverty each year has been remarkably constant, at about 12%. Income figures for each year were taken from the March Current Population Survey of that year; the cutoff for poverty was based on official government definitions. To what extent do these data support the theory of the permanent underclass? Discuss briefly.

Question 4. *[Pass rate is 86%.]*

The scatter diagram at the top of the next page shows ages of husbands and wives in Ohio. Data were extracted from the March 1993 Current Population Survey. Or did something go wrong? Explain your answer.

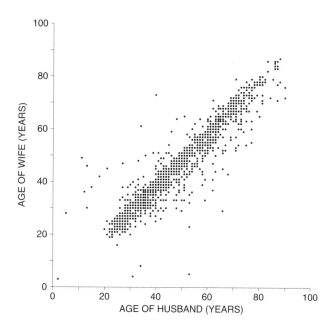

Question 5. *[Pass rate is 96%.]*

Data on the heights of fathers and sons can be summarized as follows:

average height of fathers = 68 inches,   SD = 2.7 inches
average height of sons = 69 inches,   SD = 2.7 inches, $r = 0.5$

The scatter diagram is football-shaped. On average, the sons of the 72-inch fathers were _____ 6 inches taller than the sons of the 66-inch fathers. Fill in the blank, using one of the options below, and explain your reasoning.

(i)   just about

(ii)   somewhat more than

(iii) somewhat less than

Question 6. *[Pass rate is 72%.]*

A statistician is following a group of undergraduates. On average, these students drink 4 beers a month, with an SD of 8. They eat 4 pizzas a month, with an SD of 4. There is some positive association between beer and pizza, and the regression equation is

predicted number of beers = _____ × number of pizzas + 2.

However, the statistician lost the data and forgot the slope of the equation. (Perhaps he had too much beer and pizza.) Can you help him remember the slope? Explain.

Question 7. *[Pass rate is 98%.]*

A coin is tossed 10 times.

 (a) The chance of getting 10 heads in a row is _____.
 (b) Given that the first 9 tosses were heads, the chance of getting 10 heads in a row is _____.

Explain your answers.

Question 8. *[Pass rate is 90%.]*

Twenty-five draws are made at random with replacement from the box

$$\boxed{0}\ \boxed{2}\ \boxed{3}\ \boxed{4}\ \boxed{6}$$

 (a) Fill in the blanks with a word or phrase; be clear:

   the SE for the _____ is 10, and

   the SE for the _____ is 0.40.

 (b) The figure below is a probability histogram for the sum of the draws. Fill in the blanks with numbers.

Explain your answers.

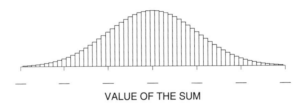

VALUE OF THE SUM

Question 9. *[Pass rate is 76%.]*

A large number of people get together. Each one draws 132 times at random with replacement from a box that has 1 red marble and 3 greens. About what percentage of these people should get 33 red marbles? Show work.

Question 10. *[Pass rate is 60%.]*

A city government did a survey of working women, to see how they felt about juggling jobs and family responsibilities. Businesses, unions, and community service organizations helped distribute the survey questionnaire to locations where the women could pick up copies. 1,678 out of 2,800 respondents, or 59.9%, checked the item "stress is a serious problem" on the questionnaire. Choose one option, and explain.

 (i)   The standard error on the 59.9% can be computed as follows:

$$\sqrt{2,800} \times \sqrt{0.599 \times .401} \approx 26, \qquad \frac{26}{2,800} \times 100\% \approx 0.9 \text{ of } 1\%$$

 (ii) The standard error on the 59.9% can be computed some other way.

 (iii) Neither of the above.

Question 11. [Pass rate is 42%.]

One month, the Current Population Survey interviewed 54,000 households, and estimated that 94.2% of all households in the US had telephones. Choose one option, and explain.

(i)   The standard error on the 94.2% can be computed as follows:

$$\sqrt{54{,}000} \times \sqrt{0.942 \times .058} \approx 54, \qquad \frac{54}{54{,}000} \times 100\% \approx 0.1 \text{ of } 1\%$$

(ii)   The standard error on the 94.2% can be computed some other way.

(iii) Neither of the above.

Question 12. *[Pass rate is 94%.]*

A laboratory makes 25 repeated measurements on the molecular weight of a protein (in "kilo-Daltons"). The average is 119, and the SD is 15. The lab now wants to estimate the likely size of certain chance errors. Fill in the blanks, using the options below; some options will be left over. You may assume the Gauss model, with no bias. Explain your answers.

(a) The chance error in one measurement is about _____ .

(b) The chance error in the average of the measurements is about _____ .
     Options:

$$15/25 \qquad 15/\sqrt{25} \qquad 15 \qquad 15 \times \sqrt{25} \qquad 15 \times 25$$

Question 13. *[Pass rate is 82%.]*

One hundred draws are made at random with replacement from a box of tickets; each ticket has a number written on it. The average of the draws is 29 and the SD of the draws is 40. You see a statistician make the following calculation:

$$z = \frac{29 - 20}{4} = 2.25, \qquad P \approx 1\%$$

(a) She seems to be testing the null hypothesis that the average of the _____ is 20. Options: box, sample.

(b) True or false: there is about a 1% chance for the null hypothesis to be right.

Explain briefly.

Question 14. *[Pass rate is 52%.]*

Can people predict how well they will behave? Do predictions influence behavior? One experiment contrasted responses to 'prediction-request" and to "request-only" treatments. In the prediction-request group, subjects were first asked to predict whether they would agree to do some volunteer work. Then they were requested to do the work. In the request-only group, the subjects were requested to do the work; they were not asked to make predictions beforehand. In parts (a-b-c), a two-sample z-test may or may not be legitimate. If it is legitimate, make it. If not, why not?

(a) 46 residents of Bloomington, Indiana were chosen at random for the "prediction-request" treatment. They were called and asked to predict "whether they would agree to spend 3 hours collecting for the American Cancer Society if contacted over the telephone with such a request." 22 out of the 46 said that they would. Another 46 residents of that town were chosen at random for the "request-only" treatment: they were requested to spend the 3 hours collecting for the American Cancer Society. Only 2 out of 46 agreed to do it. Can the difference between 22/46 and 2/46 be due to chance? What do you conclude?

(b) Three days later, the prediction-request group was called again, and requested to spend 3 hours collecting for the American Cancer Society: 14 out of 46 agreed to do so. Can the difference between 14/46 and 2/46 be due to chance? What do you conclude?

(c) Can the difference between 22/46 and 14/46 be due to chance? What do you conclude?

STATISTICS 2
FALL 1995

Mr. PURVES
MIDTERM I

Print your name _____

Sign your name _____

TA's Name _____

Lab time _____

To get full credit, you must give reasons and/or show work.

This test was given to 320 students; the percentage getting half marks or better is shown for each question, as the "pass rate."

Question 1. *[Pass rate is 33%.]*

The quotation below is taken from an article that appeared in the New York Times of December 3, 1991.

> The new research also demonstrates that spanking, which remains parents' main disciplinary weapon, is not only useless in the long run but also potentially hurtful to the child's emerging personality. In experimental studies with toddlers placed in a room with their mothers and breakable objects they were told not to touch, the children who were frequently spanked were less obedient than the children who were disciplined in nonphysical ways.

(a) Do the experimental studies mentioned in the quotation provide good evidence that children who are spanked frequently tend to become more disobedient than children who are disciplined in non-physical ways? Answer yes or no, and explain briefly.

(b) There is a precaution the investigators should have taken when doing these experiments. What is it?

Question 2. *[Pass rate is 85%.]*

A distribution table is shown below. The table gives the distribution of cholesterol level for 6,000 children, 4 to 19 years old. Cholesterol level is measured in milligrams. (More technically, it is the amount of cholesterol, in milligrams, per 100 milliliters of blood). The class intervals include the left endpoint, but exclude the right one.

Cholesterol (in milligrams)	Percent
0–140	18
140–180	52
180–200	20
200–240	10

(a) Plot the histogram. Show all intermediate work. Mark the horizontal and vertical scales carefully. Label the axes.

(b) Check one option below.

_____ The average is smaller than 120 milligrams.

_____ The average is bigger than 120 milligrams.

_____ There is not enough information to decide.

Explain your choice.

Question 3. *[Pass rate is 52%.]*

An aerobic study involves 1,040 men, age 18 to 24. The histogram of systolic blood pressure for these men followed the normal curve closely. The average is 120 mm, and 600 of the men have blood pressures between 110 and 130 mm. How many men have blood pressures between 115 and 125 mm?

Question 4. *[Pass rate is 94%.]*

(a) What is the correlation coefficient for the data set below?

x	y
0	1
0	3
1	7
1	9
1	13
3	15

(b) If possible, fill in the two blanks so that the correlation will be equal to the correlation for the data given in part (a). If this is not possible, explain why not.

x	y
0	3
0	—
1	13
1	—
1	9
3	15

Question 5. *[Pass rate is 66%.]*

For the first-year students at a certain university, the average GPA was 2.6 and the SD was 0.6. The correlation between SAT scores and first-year GPA was 0.46. The SAT scores followed the normal curve. Estimate the average first-year GPA for students whose percentile rank on the SAT was 77%.

Question 6. *[Pass rate is 14%.]*

As part of a longitudinal study of personality change, 2,500 subjects were given a psychological test twice; once at age 21, and the second time at age 35. At both ages the average score was 50, and the SD was 10. There was a strong positive association between the two scores. For each of the 2,500 subjects, the investigators used the regression method to predict score at age 35 from score at age 21. The predicted score turned out to be within 10 points of the actual score for _____ of the 2,500 subjects. Check (✓) the best option below to fill in the blank. Explain your choice.

_____ more than 68%

_____ around 68%

_____ less than 68%

Question 7. *[Pass rate is 48%.]*

From a study of 1,078 families:

$$\text{average height of father} = 68 \text{ inches}, \qquad SD = 2.7 \text{ inches}$$
$$\text{average height of son} = 69 \text{ inches}, \qquad SD = 2.7 \text{ inches}$$
$$\text{correlation coefficient} = 0.50$$

(a) Of all the sons in the study, about what percent were shorter than 69 inches?

(b) Of the sons of 68 inch fathers, about what percent were shorter than 69 inches?

(c) Of the sons of 69 inch fathers, about what percent were shorter than 70 inches?

STATISTICS 2   Mr. PURVES
FALL 1995   MIDTERM II

Print your name ——————————————————————————————

Sign your name ——————————————————————————————

TA's Name ————————————————————————————————

Lab time ——————————————————————————————————

To get full credit, you must give reasons and/or show work.

This test was given to 294 students; the percentage getting half marks or better is shown for each question, as the "pass rate."

Question 1. *[Pass rate is 38%.]*
A die is rolled twice. Find the chance that ⚀ comes up on one roll, but not both.

Question 2. *[Pass rate is 33%.]*
Box A contains 100 marbles; some are red, the rest are blue. Box B is like box A except there are twice the number of red marbles and twice the number of blue marbles. So box B contains 200 marbles. Marbles will be drawn one at a time, at random, from one of the two boxes; you win a dollar if the number of red marbles drawn is the same as the number of red marbles in the box. You are given two choices:

   (a) 100 draws with replacement will be made from box A.
   (b) 200 draws with replacement will be made from box B.

Check (✓) one of the four options below.

       _____ (a) gives a better chance of winning.

       _____ (b) gives a better chance of winning.

       _____ (a) and (b) give the same chance of winning.

       _____ Can't tell without more information.

Give reasons.

Question 3. *[Pass rate is 92%.]*
A casino offers the following game.

   The gambler stakes $1 on either spades, hearts, diamonds, or clubs. Then a deck of cards is shuffled and the top card is turned over. If the gambler stakes $1 on spades (say) and the top card is a spade, he gets his $1 back, and $2 more; if it's not a spade, he loses his $1. That ends the game. The card is put back in the deck, and the deck shuffled for the next play.

A gambler plays the game 75 times, betting on a spade each time.

(a) After 75 plays, the net gain of the gambler will be around _____,
give or take _____ or so.

(b) The gambler will win $2 on around _____ of the 75 plays, give or take
_____ or so.

Note: A deck of cards contains 52 cards: 13 spades, 13 hearts, 13 diamonds, 13
clubs.

Question 4. *[Pass rate is 80%.]*

A coin is tossed 100 times. Find the chance of getting 55 heads or 55 tails.

Question 5. *[Pass rate is 21%.]*

There are about 200 million eligible voters in the U.S. When the Gallup Poll wants
to predict the outcome of a presidential election, does it take a simple random
sample from the 200 million eligible voters? Answer yes or no. If your answers
is yes, explain why Gallup uses a simple random sample. If no, explain why Gallup
does not use a simple random sample.

Question 6. *[Pass rate is 26%.]*

At a certain university, 20% of the students have GPAs of 3.5 or better. The registrar's office is going to take a simple random of 400 students. Shown at the top
of the next page is the probability histogram for the percentage of students in the
sample with GPAs of 3.5 or better. What does the shaded area represent?

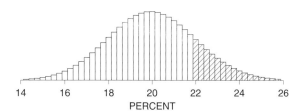

PERCENT

Question 7. *[Pass rate is 94%.]*

In a certain city, there are 10,000 men age 25–34; 225 of them are chosen at random:

$$\text{average of sample incomes} = \$24{,}200$$
$$\text{SD of sample incomes} = \$17{,}700$$

(a) Estimate the average income of all men in the city, with ages in the range
25–34.

(b) Attach an SE to your estimate.

(c) True or false, and explain: About 95% of the men age 25–34 in the city have
incomes in the range from $21,840 to $26,560.

STATISTICS 2   Mr. PURVES
FALL 1995   FINAL EXAM

Print your name ⎯⎯⎯⎯⎯⎯⎯⎯⎯⎯⎯⎯⎯⎯⎯⎯⎯⎯⎯⎯⎯⎯

Sign your name ⎯⎯⎯⎯⎯⎯⎯⎯⎯⎯⎯⎯⎯⎯⎯⎯⎯⎯⎯⎯⎯⎯

TA's Name ⎯⎯⎯⎯⎯⎯⎯⎯⎯⎯⎯⎯⎯⎯⎯⎯⎯⎯⎯⎯⎯⎯⎯⎯⎯

Lab time ⎯⎯⎯⎯⎯⎯⎯⎯⎯⎯⎯⎯⎯⎯⎯⎯⎯⎯⎯⎯⎯⎯⎯⎯⎯⎯

To get full credit, you must give reasons and/or show work.

This test was given to 292 students; the percentage getting half marks or better is shown for each question, as the "pass rate."

Question 1. *[Pass rate is 63%.]*

The paragraph below is taken from an article in the San Francisco Chronicle of Tuesday, March 21, 1995. The person quoted in the article is Patrick Portway, executive director of the United States Distance Learning Association in San Ramon, California.

> "Studies of high school students who took German by satellite from teachers at Oklahoma State University found that they consistently outperformed students taking German at their own schools," Portway noted. "The reason is that the instructor is a college German teacher. He uses music videos, German cultural films, all the media that every teacher would love to have. He has a $7.5 million TV studio at his fingertips."

Before accepting Mr. Portway's reason, what question should you ask him? State the question, and explain why it is relevant.

Question 2. *[Pass rate is 63%.]*

The quotation below is taken from an article in the San Francisco Chronicle of July 17, 1995. The department mentioned in the quote is the Justice Department. Some words and numbers have been left out.

> In a study of state civil suits in the nation's 75 largest counties, the department's Bureau of Justice Statistics found that in 1992 there were 762,000 civil suits involving torts, contracts and real property rights. Punitive damages were awarded in only 364 cases. The study found that the _____ award was about _____, brought _____ from the _____ award of _____ by a few _____ awards.

The missing words and numbers are somewhere in the following list:

average, median, up, down, large, small, $50,000, $735,000.

Fill in the blanks to complete the sentence. Explain your reasoning briefly.

Question 3. *[Pass rate is 88%.]*

More than 1 million high school students took the SAT in 1995. The average verbal score was 428 and the SD was 110.

   (a) Estimate the 60th percentile of the verbal SAT scores in 1995.

   (b) In California, the average verbal score was 417 and the SD was 110 points. About what percent of the California test takers did better than the national average?

Question 4. *[Pass rate is 84%.]*

For men age 55 to 64 in the U. S. in 1993, the relationship between education (years of schooling completed) and personal income can be summarized as follows:

$$\text{average education} = 12 \text{ years} \qquad \text{SD} = 3 \text{ years}$$
$$\text{average income} = \$38,700 \qquad \text{SD} = \$26,700$$
$$\text{correlation coefficient} = 0.45.$$

   (a) Find the regression equation for predicting income from education.

   (b) If possible with the information given, estimate the average income of men age 55 to 64 with 15 years of education. If this is impossible, explain why.

Question 5. *[Pass rate is 75%.]*

A box contains six tickets, numbered as shown:

$$\boxed{1}\ \boxed{2}\ \boxed{3}\ \boxed{4}\ \boxed{5}\ \boxed{6}$$

Three tickets are drawn at random, without replacement, from the box. Find the chance the three tickets left in the box are 4, 5 and 6.

Question 6. *[Pass rate is 30%.]*

A box contains 1,500 marbles, of which 500 are red and 1,000 are blue. The following procedure is repeated many times.

   One hundred draws are made at random with replacement from the box, and the number of red marbles in the 100 draws is counted.

The first time the procedure is done, there are 28 red marbles in the 100 draws; the next time there are 25; the third time there are 27. The results for the first 10 repetitions are shown below:

$$28 \quad 25 \quad 27 \quad 31 \quad 26 \quad 29 \quad 26 \quad 23 \quad 30 \quad 24$$

Is there any reason to be suspicious of these results? Answer yes or no. Back up your answer with reasons and/or calculations.

Question 7. *[Pass rate is 95%.]*

Harry and Sam play the following game 75 times. A die is rolled. If ⊡ comes up, Sam pays Harry $1. If ⊞ comes up, Harry pays Sam $1. If anything else comes up, no money changes hands.

(a) As far as the chances are concerned, Al's net gain from the 75 plays is like the sum of _____ draws from the box _____. Fill in the first blank with a number and the second with a box. Your box should show tickets marked with numbers.

(b) Al's net gain from the 75 plays will be around _____ give or take _____ or so.

Question 8. *[Pass rate is 23%.]*

A box contains 990 tickets marked "1" and 10 marked "2". One hundred draws are made at random, with replacement, from the box. True or false, and explain.

(a) The expected value for the sum of the 100 numbers drawn is 101.

(b) The SE for the sum is 1.0 (after rounding).

(c) There is about a 93% chance the sum will be in the range from 100 to 105 inclusive.

Question 9. *[Pass rate is 87%.]*

The distribution of rents in a small California town is shown below. For example, the second line of the table says that 5,300 of the units have rents in the range from $250 to $499. No units rent for under $100, so all the rental units in the town are represented in the table.

Monthly rent (dollars)	Number of rental units
100–249	900
250–499	5,300
500–749	9,000
750–999	3,000
1,000 plus	800

The housing office is going to take a simple random sample of 500 units from all the rental units in the town. The number of units in the sample which rent for under $750 will be around _____ give or take _____ or so.

Question 10. *[Pass rate is 44%.]*

A sociologist takes a simple random sample of 300 from the 27,000 students enrolled at a large state university. There are 222 undergraduates and 78 graduate students in the sample. So the sample percentage of undergraduates is $222/300 \times 100\% = 74\%$. The sociologist calculates the SE for the sample percentage of undergraduates, gets 2.5% as the result, and writes down the following 95%-confidence interval: 69% to 79%.

(a) True or false, and explain: The range from 69% to 79% is an approximate 95%-confidence interval for the percentage of undergraduates in the sample.

(b) True or false, and explain: The 95% is (approximately) right, because the probability histogram for the percentage of undergraduates at the university follows the normal curve closely.

(c) In the same semester, a second sociologist also takes a simple random sample of 300 students from the university, and uses the same procedure as the first sociologist to calculate a confidence interval. True or false, and explain: The second sociologist will arrive at exactly the same confidence interval as the first one.

Question 11. *[Pass rate is 20%.]*

A study involves 7,000 working couples in a certain suburb: 14,000 people in all. In one part of the study, the investigators take a simple random of 100 couples from the 7,000. In the sample, 70 of the 100 husbands earn more than $20,000, as do 46 of the wives. So 116 people in the sample earn more than $20,000. The investigators estimate that $116/200 \times 100\% = 58\%$ of the 14,000 people in the study earn more than $20,000. If possible with the information given, attach a standard error to this estimate. If this is not possible, explain why not.

Question 12. *[Pass rate is 57%.]*

Twenty-five measurements are made on the speed of light. These average out to 300,007 and the SD is 10, the units being kilometers per second. (You may assume the Gauss model with no bias.) The speed of light is estimated as _____; this estimate is likely to be off by _____ or so.

Question 13. *[Pass rate is 46%.]*

As part of a study of attitudes toward public and private schools, a simple random sample of 1,200 adults was taken from a city of 100,000 adults. The people in the sample were asked to respond to the following two questions.

Q1. "Which city schools, public or private, are generally more likely to provide better teachers?"

In the sample, 26% chose the public schools.

Q2. "Which city schools, public or private, are generally more likely to provide higher academic expectations?"

In the sample, 24% chose the public schools. Is the difference between the 26% and the 24% statistically significant?

(a) Formulate the null hypothesis in terms of a box model. To do this answer the following five questions.

    (i)   Are there one or two boxes?

    (ii) How many tickets are in the box (boxes)?

    (iii) How many draws are made?

    (iv) What do the tickets show?

    (v) What does the null hypothesis say about the box (boxes)?

(b) Is the difference statistically significant? Or can this be determined from the information given? Back up your answer with reasons and/or calculations.

Question 14. *[Pass rate is 62%.]*

The following experiment was carried out to evaluate a drug for the prevention of heart attacks. The subjects were 3,900 middle-aged men with heart trouble. Out of these men, 1,100 were assigned at random to receive the drug, and the remaining 2,800 were given a placebo. The subjects were followed for five years. In the group that received the drug, there were 220 deaths; in the control group, there were 588 deaths. The 220 is 20% of the treatment group and the 588 is 21% of the control group. Someone argues as follows: "A one-percentage-point difference may not seem like much, but 1% of a million, for example, is 10,000. The drug will save tens of thousands of lives."

(a) Calculate the appropriate test statistic and find the observed significance level.

(b) Do you agree with the claim that the drug will save tens of thousands of lives? Answer yes or no and explain.